A PROMISE TO KEEP

A Promise to Keep

By JAMES D. SMART

Illustrated by J. M. Swanson

THE
WESTMINSTER PRESS
PHILADELPHIA

Printed in the United States of America
at The Lakeside Press
R. R. Donnelley & Sons Company, Chicago
and Crawfordsville, Indiana

CONTENTS

GOD'S PLAN—A Prologue

The story of the Bible is about God, but it is also about you. It tells what God has been doing in the world from the very beginning to draw all men and women and children into one family that would love and serve him. It tells you and all the people of the earth how you can be his family today.

On the very first page of the Bible you read that God made the world, that he made everything in it. The story does not tell about the hundreds of thousands of years in which the world and the stars were growing and changing or about the long ages in the life of man upon the earth. Those things were not known by men in ancient times. The Bible tells you what is much more important—that the whole world belongs to God, and that God has made you so that you can take your place in it and care for it. But he has made you free to choose whether you will live in it as he wants you to live or whether you will go your own way and do as you please.

Turn a page in your Bible and in the third chapter of Genesis you find a story of a man who decided he could get what he wanted much better if he disobeyed God than if he obeyed him. But when he did it, he had a great disappointment. One trouble after another came upon him. He could no longer live as one of God's family if he did not obey God. When you read that story, you know that it could be about any one of us.

Then come other stories of men who chose to disobey God. In doing so they became divided from each other and lived in fear and hatred. The day seemed far away when all men would know that they were God's people and would live together in peace and good will. But God was not willing to let men defeat his plan. It might take hundreds, or even thousands, of years, but he would one day carry it through. The way to begin was to choose a man who would be faithful to him and whose family would learn to be faithful. Then, through them, others would come to know God and serve him too.

So God chose Abraham, and after many years the family of Abraham became the people of Israel. They were not always faithful to God; often they forgot him almost completely. But again and again he spoke to them through men called prophets, reminding them of his plan and warning them that unless they lived in his ways they would bring much unhappiness upon themselves.

At last God had to do something more than he had done before. Because he loved all men even when they forgot him and disobeyed him, he sent into the world his own Son, Jesus Christ, that he might draw them back to him. When Jesus grew up, he told men the good news that they could begin to live at once as God's true people. Men who loved their own ways better than God's ways hated him and put him to death. Even to the followers of Jesus it seemed as though God's plan had failed. But soon they

8

knew they were wrong. Jesus still lived. And as men and women and children all across the world heard the story of his life and death, more and more of them loved him and became his followers. God, in a new way, was carrying out his plan.

The story is not yet finished. The world is still far from being what God wants it to be. Even though the Church of Jesus Christ now circles the whole earth, there are many people who do not understand God's plan. But you may understand it as you read the story of what God has been doing from the very beginning. You too may learn what your part is in this plan for the whole world.

1. Choosing a People

ABRAHAM hurried through the narrow streets of Haran toward the city gate. From the open booths, first on one side, then on the other, came the cries of the merchants calling their wares—richly colored silks, pottery, metals, sweetmeats. He did not stop but hurried on to the great open square.

In the shadow of the tower that rose high above the gate were the tables of the scribes, who spent most of their time writing letters and business agreements for other people. Abraham chose one of them and began to dictate a letter.

"To Nahor, in Ur in the land of Chaldea. Peace and blessing unto you, my brother. Terah our father has died and I plan now to go far away to another land. Our nephew Lot will go with me. Come at once that all that belonged to Terah our father may be yours."

As Abraham spoke, the scribe wrote with a three-cornered wooden stick on a little tablet of clay which he held in the palm of his hand. When he had finished, he baked the tablet to make it hard and wrapped it in another piece of clay like an envelope, to keep it from being damaged. The next caravan would take Abraham's letter more than six hundred miles to Ur.

Three months later Nahor, tired and dusty from his long journey, arrived in Haran. Sarah, Abraham's wife, set food before him, and as he ate he began to question Abraham.

"What is this foolish thing you plan to do? It is not many years since you went out from the home of our fathers in Ur. You settled in Haran and you have prospered here. But now you want to leave Haran even as once you left Ur."

Abraham answered quietly.

"You know well why we could not stay in Ur. We

could no longer worship the same gods as our neighbors. The things that are done in the temple of Nannar, the moon-god, are wrong. And because we knew that they were wrong we could not go there. The most high God has shown me that he is great and good and true, and not false and cruel as most men seem to think. But our neighbors in Ur were angry that my family and I did not follow their ways. In Haran it has been no better."

Nahor did not speak for a moment; then he said:

"I do not understand you. The gods of Ur and Haran are good enough for me. But since you are determined to go, I will do what I can to help you."

Not many days later, early in the morning, a caravan moved slowly westward. Soon the walls of Haran faded into the distance.

A long line of camels and donkeys carried the baggage. Some of the camels carried women and children also, upon packsaddles made of goatskin tents or soft rugs. These were led by menservants, while others tended the flocks and herds that moved slowly over the barren ground. Leaders of the tribe rode ahead with Abraham.

The caravan did not move far each day, for pasture had to be found for the sheep and cattle. Each night the women unloaded the great black tents of goatskin and pitched them, spreading out carpets on the ground for beds inside the tents. The fires were lighted, and supper was made ready. It was easy to tell which tent was Abraham's, for it was the largest of them all.

Over the mountains and across wide plains they traveled. Sometimes they went for days through desert country. Then at last they came to a land where there were high hills and beautiful valleys and where pasture was no longer hard to find. This was Canaan. Much of the land belonged to tribes that were not friendly to strangers. But there was room for Abraham and Lot and all the people with them.

When the caravan reached Shechem, Abraham called all the people about him.

"This is the land toward which God has been leading us," he said, "and this will be our home for years to come."

Then Abraham called upon his men to gather stones to build an altar near a giant oak. And there he prayed for his people to the God who had led him out from Haran. "Be with my people in this new land, O mighty God. Show us how we may truly serve thee."

Abraham and his people did not always stay in one place in the Land of Canaan. They went wherever the pasture was best. In some years there was no rain to make the grass grow, and both the people and the flocks became very hungry. But Abraham knew what to do. He led them southward into the land of Egypt, where water from the River Nile made grass and grain grow even in the driest years. Then when times were better in Canaan he led them back again.

gave him a new name—Israel. God promised him that he would be the father of a great people.

In the morning Esau came riding to meet him, and Jacob saw in his eyes, not hatred, but a glad welcome for him and his family. Then Jacob knew that God had prepared the way for him to return to Canaan.

When Jacob was an old man, there was a terrible famine in Canaan, and it seemed as though everyone would starve. But God provided food and a new home for his people in a way they could never have expected.

Years before this time of famine there had been a quarrel among Jacob's sons. Joseph, who was younger than the others, made them angry by saying that he had dreamed of a day when he would be ruler over all of them. They said, "Let us get rid of this dreamer before he makes us his servants." So they sold him as a slave to merchantmen who were journeying toward Egypt. In Egypt, however, people learned that Joseph was wise and honest, and after many adventures he rose to be the chief man next to the Pharaoh himself. In preparation for a time of famine he built huge storehouses and stored great quantities of grain.

When food became scarce in Canaan, Jacob's sons went to Egypt to buy grain. They did not know that Joseph still lived. They did not know that he was in charge of all the stores of grain. But as soon as Joseph saw them he recognized them. First he tested them to see if they had changed their ways. Then he forgave them the wrong they had done to him and sent them to bring Jacob and all their families to Egypt.

When the famine was over, the people still lived on in a district called Goshen in the north of Egypt, for things went well with them there. But Jacob could not forget how God had promised that Canaan was to be the home of his people. When he was dying he said to Joseph, "God will be with you, and one day he will lead you back to the land of your fathers."

In Egypt the sons of Jacob were called Israelites, because of the new name that God had given Jacob. For many years they did not want to go back to Canaan. It was pleasanter where they were. Long years passed, and they increased greatly in number. Then came a time when it was no longer pleasant for them in Egypt and they would have been happy to see the brown hills of Canaan. The Egyptians now had forgotten even the name of Joseph and they made the Israelites become their slaves. But many of the Israelites as they lived among the Egyptians had forgotten something more important. They had forgotten the God of Abraham and of Isaac and of Jacob.

When the Pharaoh had a new storehouse or a new city to build, he would say: "Let these Israelites carry the heaviest stones for the walls. It does not matter if their strength is broken." When he heard that their number was increasing, he gave orders: "Let every man-child that is born among these slaves be killed." The Israelites feared that their people would be completely destroyed. But God did not intend to let them perish. When their days were darkest, God was already preparing a way to deliver them and to lead them to their own land.

A young Israelite named Moses had been adopted by a princess of the royal court. He grew up in Pharaoh's household and was educated as a prince. He was taken to the great pillared temples of the Egyptian gods, but all the time he remembered what his Israelite mother had taught him about the God of Abraham and of Isaac and of Jacob. He had little joy in the comforts and delights of the royal palaces as long as he saw his own people whipped and made to serve as slaves.

One day when Moses was walking in the city, he came upon an Egyptian taskmaster beating an Israelite slave. Striking the Egyptian down, Moses killed him. When this became known, he had to flee from the country. He went eastward across the land of Sinai to the shepherd country of Midian and lived there many years. In Midian he made his home with Jethro, a priest. Jethro's daughter, Zipporah, became his wife and they had two sons. But Moses thought again and again of what his people were suffering back in Egypt.

One day as Moses was tending sheep in the green pastures of the mountainside suddenly he knew that God was very near to him. Moses saw what seemed to be a bush burning with fire and yet never burning away. Then God spoke to him:

"I am the God of Abraham, the God of Isaac, and the God of Jacob. I have chosen you to speak for me as my prophet and to lead my people out of Egypt that I may deliver them from their slavery."

Moses answered: "Who am I to do so great a thing as this? I am not a good speaker and I am too weak."

But God rebuked him for his fears and promised to go with him to teach him what he should say and do.

At once Moses journeyed to Egypt. Going to Pharaoh, he demanded that the Israelites should be set free to return to Canaan. He pleaded again and again with Pharaoh, but Pharaoh would not let them go. Then strange things happened in Egypt. The waters of the Nile became red and poisonous; there came plagues of frogs and lice and flies. Cattle died. A great earthquake shook the land. The Egyptians were afraid, and at last Pharaoh sent for Moses. *Now* it was Pharaoh who pleaded.

"Ask your God to stop these terrible things and I will let your people go," he said.

But Pharaoh did not keep his promise. Better days came, but the Israelites were still slaves in Egypt.

Then suddenly a still worse disaster came upon the Egyptians. In every family the oldest son died. Pharaoh sent again for Moses.

"Take your Israelites and all their possessions and leave this land at once," he commanded. "When you are gone, there will perhaps be an end to our misfortunes."

Not a moment was lost. Messengers carried the word to every Israelite home. Far into the night everyone worked to get ready, for tomorrow Israel would be free.

The road eastward was a hard one through dry and barren country. The sun beat down upon the travelers and they became tired and thirsty. But if they began to go more slowly, Moses sent word to make haste.

Day and night they marched toward the border, stopping only to eat and to take a few hours of rest. At last they came to the shore of an inland sea. There on the other side was the land of Sinai, where they would be safe.

The Israelites camped on the shore. It was good to lie down and rest their tired bodies.

Suddenly there was a cry from one of the watchmen:

"The Egyptians are coming!"

In the distance across the flat country they could see chariots moving at a furious pace. The Israelites had no chariots. They had no weapons with which to fight. There seemed to be nothing they could do. Some of them turned angrily to Moses:

"Have you brought us all this way through the desert just to die? We would have been wiser to stay in Egypt. Where is this God that you said would lead us?"

Moses answered them: "Have no fear. God will make a way for us."

Then, as Moses prayed, he heard God saying to him, "Speak now to the Children of Israel and tell them to go forward, for I will be with them and will deliver them."

That night a strong east wind blew upon the waters and laid bare a shallow place by which the Israelites crossed safely to the other side. But when the Egyptians with their chariots tried to follow, their wheels sank in the soft mud and the waters, returning, swept them into the deep, where they were drowned.

Among the Israelites some who had grumbled now said: "What Moses told us is true. God is with us indeed. He has power to make a way where there seems to be no way."

2. The Promise

MOST of the fires before the tent doors had died away to ashes, but the fire before Moses' tent burned brightly. Everyone in the camp knew what a happy day it had been for Moses. His father-in-law, Jethro, had come from Midian, bringing with him Moses' wife, and their two sons. They had been sent to Midian for safety, but when word came that the Israelites had escaped from Egypt and were already in the mountains of Sinai, the boys with their mother and grandfather set out to find the camp. That day at noon they had come over the last ridge and had seen with joy the tents of the Israelites on the broad plain at the foot of the mountains.

The light of the fire flickered upon the faces of Moses and Jethro as they sat talking. Moses' brother, Aaron, was with them too. First Jethro had to hear the story of how God had brought the Israelites out of Egypt. Then Moses told him of the long hard journey through the desert, and what a struggle it had been to keep the people from turning back in discouragement. Sometimes their throats had been parched with thirst. Sometimes they had thought they would starve. But God had not failed them. In wonderful ways they had found food and water when they needed them most.

When Jethro heard the story, he said, "Now I know that the Lord is greater than all gods, greater by far than the gods of the Egyptians." When morning came, he called together all the older men with Moses and Aaron to offer a sacrifice upon the altar and to give thanks to God for his care over his people.

All day long Moses sat in his tent, and the people came to him with their disputes and hard questions. There was no one whom they trusted as they did Moses. Then, in the evening, Moses and Jethro sat again before the fire.

"Moses, it is not good that you alone give guidance to the people," said Jethro. "You have too much work. You will kill yourself if you continue in this way, and then what will the people do?"

"They come to ask what is God's will for them," answered Moses. "How can I turn them away?"

"There is a better way," said Jethro. "Your task is to give your heart and mind to God that he may teach you his will for his people. But choose out true and unselfish men that they may be leaders under you. When they have been taught by you, they will be guides to the people and will settle their disputes."

Before Jethro returned to his home in Midian, Moses did as he advised. He chose elders to share with him in leading the Israelites and thus was able to give his time to more important things.

Often Moses went out from the camp and climbed high up the mountain that he might be alone with God. He knew that God had a great plan for his people, but he must know what God wanted them to do.

One day when he came down from the mountain he called together the elders and the people in a great open space in the camp.

"You have asked me what lies before us and what we must do," said Moses, looking round on the men and women and children who three months before had been slaves in Egypt. "The God who set us free from slavery and led us safely all the way from Egypt is still our God. And because he is our God, a great future is before us. He has chosen us to be his people. Therefore we must make a covenant with him and promise that we will serve him all our days."

Then all the people answered together and said: "All that the Lord has asked of us we will do. If he will be our God, then we will be his people."

Again Moses went up the mountainside and was gone for many days. When he returned he had two tablets of stone with ten commandments written upon them which he had received from God.

As Moses came near the camp, he heard a great noise. Then he saw people dancing around a golden calf and bowing down before it as though it were a god. Moses called Aaron to him.

"What does this mean?" he demanded.

Aaron was frightened at Moses' anger. "The people came to me," he said, "and asked me to make them a god whom they could see and worship. You were so long upon the mountain that they thought you would never come back again."

"You made a god for them!" cried Moses. "Do you not know that the God we serve is the Maker of all things? There can be no likeness of him in any image of gold or wood or stone!"

Then Moses broke the two tablets of stone so that they could not be read, and he told the people how deeply they had sinned against God. But when he was alone with God, Moses prayed for the people that they might be forgiven.

So the days passed, and the Israelites began to learn that they must obey God if they would be his people. And when they were ready, Moses brought to them other tablets of stone with the Commandments of God written upon them. But because the people were so slow to learn God's ways, they had to stay in the wilderness for many years. It was a life of struggle and hardship.

Moses wanted the people to have a place to worship God, so he built a Tabernacle, a great tent which was always the first one to be pitched in the camp. Aaron was made priest over the Tabernacle, with the tribe of Levi to help him. When the people came to worship, they saw a large wooden chest that was called the Ark. In the Ark, they knew, were the two tablets of stone that Moses had brought down from the mountain.

"Make ready to move northward." The word went quickly through the camp. Years had passed since Israel first saw the mountain of Sinai. Moses was old now, and Joshua, his chief captain, led the people. Many who had come from Egypt with Moses had died. But the hundreds of men and women and children who had been born in the wilderness knew nothing of Egypt and its ways. Moses and the elders had taught them the ways of God.

Year after year Moses had talked of the land that God had promised should be their home. It was a day of great joy as the caravan began to move toward Canaan. But even now a whisper went from one to the other: "All our troubles are not over yet. They say there are giants in Canaan who will slay us if we try to enter."

There *were* troubles. When the caravan tried to move into Canaan directly from the south, fierce tribes blocked the way. They turned eastward to the border of Edom and sent messengers to the king of Edom, saying, "Let us pass through your land and we will pay you well for what our sheep and cattle may eat by the way." But the answer that came back was: "No! You shall not pass my border."

So began another weary journey—south through the desert and around the borders of Edom, then north

through Moab to the borders of the kingdom of Sihon.
When Sihon tried to stop them they fought against
him and defeated him. On they went until at last
they stood on the great hills east of the Jordan Valley.
Across the valley they could see the hills of Canaan.

Moses called Joshua to him, and all the people
gathered round.

"Joshua, from this day you will be the leader of
Israel in my place," said Moses. "It is not God's will
for me to go any farther. My brother Aaron and
many who helped me have died. But God in his mercy
has let me look on the hills of Canaan from afar."

In a few days Moses was dead.

Soon after Moses died, Joshua made ready to cross into Canaan. First he sent messengers to call the men whose tribes had already found land for themselves in the hills north of Moab. Then the women cooked food to last for many days. The warriors made sure that their gear was ready for battle.

It did not take long to cross the Jordan, for the water was held back and they easily found a shallow place. Across the river the city of Jericho fell into their hands quickly and the way was open for them to move up the valleys to the highlands above. That was the beginning of many battles.

Messages went from Jerusalem to Hebron and from Hebron to Lachish. To every city north and south the word was carried. "A strange people have invaded our land and already the city of Ai has fallen to them." "The Gibeonites in fear have made a treaty with them." "Before it is too late, let us join our armies together and drive these strangers out."

But Joshua's army was too strong for the kings of the Canaanite cities to stand against it. So the tribes of Israel found new homes in Canaan. There were twelve tribes in all, each bearing the name of one of the sons of Jacob. Some of them, who already had captured land to the east of the Jordan, went back to their homes there.

The Israelites did not drive out all the Canaanites. Often they lived as neighbors with the people who had been there before them. Then Joshua was afraid, for the Canaanites worshiped false gods and knew nothing of the laws of God that Moses had given his people. It was easy for the Israelites, now that they were scattered through the land, to forget their God.

When there was peace in the land, Joshua called elders from all the tribes to meet with him at Shechem. Then he showed them how, since the time of Abraham, God had been leading his people.

"Now that you have homes in this land, take care that you do not forget the Lord your God," he said to them. "Be sure to remember all the laws that Moses gave you. If you forget and begin to do as the Canaanites do and to serve false gods, God will turn away from you and you will perish. Today you must choose whom you will serve. *My* choice is made. No matter what others may do, I and all that live with me in my house will serve the Lord."

The answer of the elders that day was like the voice of one man: "We will serve the Lord our God and his voice will we obey."

The tribes of Israel did not always keep the promise that they made to God at Shechem. Their children played in the fields with the children of the Canaanites. Their sons and daughters married the sons and daughters of the Canaanites. When there were good things to eat and drink in the shrines of the Canaanite gods, the Israelites went with their neighbors. Little by little they became like the other people of the land; they forgot what it meant to be God's people.

Then came times of trouble. Jabin, king of Hazor, marched down from the north with an army. For twenty years he oppressed the Israelites. They seemed to have no strength to stand against him. It was then that Deborah, a woman of great faith, called the tribes together. She sent word to them that she and Barak would be their leaders to drive Jabin from the land.

The next danger was from nearer at hand. The Philistines marched up into the hills from their cities on the lowland plain along the shore of the Mediterranean Sea. Their armies were so strong that for many years they kept the Israelites subject to them. At times a leader would call the tribes together and they would rebel against the Philistines. But only too often this made their troubles not less but greater than before.

At Shiloh there was a shrine where people from all the tribes came to worship God. The Tabernacle had been set up at Shiloh when the Israelites first came into Canaan. The Ark was there, which always reminded the people of their promise to God and of the laws that Moses had received from God. But at Shiloh the laws of God were sometimes forgotten, and even the priests who were supposed to care for the shrine and lead the people in worship did things that were evil. There did not seem to be anyone in those days who could tell the people clearly what God wanted them to do.

The Israelites in all the tribes were glad when they heard about the young priest Samuel at Shiloh.

"He is more than a priest," they said. "He is a prophet like Moses, and he is able, like Joshua, to lead us against our enemies."

Samuel had lived at the shrine in Shiloh since he was a boy, but he was different from the other priests. Many of them did not care what happened to the

people. All they wanted was plenty to eat. But Samuel's one desire was to listen for what God would say to him and to show the people the way in which they should go. Samuel told them that all their troubles had come upon them because they had not kept the promise that their fathers had made to God.

So began a new day for Israel. With Samuel to lead them, they became united and strong. It seemed as though the more loyal they were to God the more loyal they were to each other. The Philistines said: "What has happened to these people? We had them as our subjects, but now they are driving us out of their land."

The Israelites saw a way to make their nation stronger still, and they came to Samuel with a request that did not please him:

"Give us a king to rule us and to lead us in battle. Then we shall be able to conquer the Philistines and we shall be like other kingdoms."

Samuel told the people that God was their king and warned them what would happen. "A king will want a great army and he will take your sons to be his soldiers. A king will want a palace and he will take your daughters to be his serving-women. A king will need supplies and he will take a tenth of all your cattle and grain and fruit. It would be better for you to have no king but God."

But when he saw that the people were determined to have a king, Samuel chose a young man named Saul and anointed him in the name of God to be king over Israel. Saul was taller than any other man in Israel and he was as strong and brave as he was tall. But Samuel told him that if he was to lead Israel aright, his first care must be to obey God.

So Saul became king. First he gathered an army strong enough to drive the Philistines out of the hill country. The Israelites on the borders of the land were no longer afraid of their neighboring countries, for they said, "If anyone tries to harm us, Saul will come with his army and rescue us."

But Samuel watched always to see whether or not the people and the king would keep their covenant with God. He said to himself: "Saul cares more for his power and for the glory of his victories than he cares for God. If he does not obey God, God will reject him from being king."

3. When Kings Forget

DAVID! DAVID!"

David got up from where he was sitting as he watched the sheep and climbed a near-by hill to see who was calling him. He recognized one of the servants from home and ran to meet him. The man, out of breath from running, could hardly speak.

"Your father—and the prophet—they want you—go quickly!"

When David came where his father, Jesse, and his brothers were waiting with the prophet Samuel, he felt at once that something very important was happening. Samuel greeted David, and then stood quietly with his sharp eyes upon him as though he were waiting for something.

At last Samuel turned to Jesse and spoke: "This is the one whom the Lord has chosen. I will anoint him now. The day will come when he shall be king over all Israel." Then he turned to David and said, "When that day comes, see that you obey the voice of God in all things."

Young David went back to tend his sheep. Often in the quiet of the hills he thought of what it meant that God had chosen him to lead his people in the days to come.

After a time there was war again with the Philistines. The armies were drawn up on opposite sides of the broad valley of Elah, ready for battle. Sometimes, in those days, instead of whole armies fighting and many men being killed, each army chose a champion to fight for it. The army of the champion who won was given the victory. The Philistines had as their champion a giant of a man, Goliath. The Israelites had no one with courage to stand against him.

David's brothers were in Saul's army, and David had been sent to them with a supply of food from home. They were surprised and angry when they heard that, unknown to them, David had offered to go out against Goliath. David might be taller and stronger than most men, but he was still a youth and not even a soldier. Their hearts sank when they saw him moving down the hill toward Goliath. He carried no armor to protect him—nothing except his shepherd's sling.

But that day the shepherd's sling was stronger than the giant's sword. With a round stone that he took from the river bed, David struck down the champion of the Philistines and brought victory to the army of Saul.

From that day King Saul chose David to be a captain in his army and to live with him in his palace. Often David played upon his harp and sang to Saul. No one was more admired and praised by the people than David.

One of Saul's sons, Jonathan, became David's friend from the day he came to live in the king's house. They were friends in all things. They promised each other that nothing should ever separate them.

As the people saw that David was brave and strong and a wise leader, they began to say that he was an even greater man than Saul. Then Saul became jealous of David, and because he feared David he also hated him. Jonathan tried to protect his friend; but when he could no longer do so, David had to hide in the hills of southern Judah or he would have been killed.

For a time David and a band of men who followed him lived in the cave of Adullam in the southern hills. Then for some years they served as soldiers to protect the Philistine city of Ziklag. But never would David let any of his men do harm to Saul or to the people of Israel. And among the Israelites David was not forgotten.

One day as David was sitting in his camp in Ziklag, a messenger came running. As soon as he saw David, he cried out,

"Saul and Jonathan have been killed in battle on Mount Gilboa!"

It was sad news for David, for he loved Jonathan more than any other man. But it meant also that the day had come for him to be king.

Quickly his men made ready and, with their families, moved up through the hills to Hebron. At Hebron the two tribes of the south country gathered together and made David king. But in the north country and across the Jordan the ten other tribes chose a son of Saul to be their king. Then there were unhappy years when the tribes of Israel fought against each other.

After seven years the tribes of the north saw that David was the better king, and they sent their leaders to Hebron to say to him, "You shall be king over all Israel, and there shall no longer be war between us."

In all the years since the Israelites marched into Canaan with Joshua, they had not been able to capture the city of Jerusalem. Its walls were so strong and the sides of the hill on which it was built were so steep that it did not seem as though any army could ever take it. But David decided that Jerusalem should be his capital city, for it was right in the center of the land between the tribes of the north and the tribes of the south. He captured it by sending his men up a secret passage which ran, from a spring on the hillside, under the walls and into the city.

Then David built a palace of cedar for himself in his new city. He also brought to Jerusalem the Ark which had once been in Shiloh. He chose good men to lead the people. If a wrong was done to any man, the man came at once to David, for he knew the king would try to make it right. So the people of Israel grew strong and were no longer subject to any other nation.

As the years went by, David's power became greater and greater. Countries round about were conquered by his armies. There seemed to be nothing that David could not do. Once he had been a shepherd, but now he was rich and powerful and could have whatever he wanted.

Near David's house lived a man named Uriah, who was one of David's soldiers. He had marched away with the army to fight the Ammonites. His wife, Bath-sheba, was very beautiful. When David saw

Bath-sheba one day, he wished that she could be his wife. Then an evil plan came to his mind. He would send word for Uriah to be put in the front line of battle. The soldiers in the front line were almost always killed, and one of them might as well be Uriah!

Soon a messenger was on his way to the commander of the army. And after the battle only David and the commander knew why Uriah was one of those who had died. Then David married Bath-sheba.

But David had forgotten about God and about the Prophet Nathan who spoke in the name of God.

Nathan came into the royal court while David was listening to people who were appealing to him for justice. This was not the first time the prophet had come to tell him of a wrong that had been done, and David listened patiently as Nathan told his story.

"There were two men in the city," Nathan began. "The one was rich and the other poor. The rich man had many sheep and cattle. The poor man had nothing except a pet lamb, which he and his children cared for each day as though it were a little child. Now this rich man had a visitor come to his house, and he wanted to make a fine dinner for him. But he didn't take one of his own sheep. No! He went down to the poor man's house, and took his pet lamb, and killed it to make the dinner for his guest!"

David's face grew dark with anger as he heard the story. When it was finished, he rose from his seat and gave his judgment.

"The man who did this cruel thing shall surely die, and the poor man shall be given four lambs for the one that was taken from him."

Slowly Nathan's hand rose until his finger was pointing straight at David. "*You* are the man," he said. "You had no pity when you sent Uriah out to die and when you took his wife. God chose you to be king, but you have scorned God in doing this thing."

Suddenly David was no longer proud of his power and his wealth. He knew that even though he was king he could not do whatever he liked. He would have only sorrow unless he obeyed God. He answered Nathan humbly, "I have sinned against the Lord."

Then Nathan told him that God would forgive him, but that he would have to bear great troubles because of the wrong he had done.

Years passed and David's sons were now grown men. The one whom David loved best was Absalom. But Absalom was not loyal to his father. He planned how he might win the people to follow him and so become king in place of his father.

David was in the palace one day when a messenger came who had run nineteen miles from Hebron.

"Absalom has won the hearts of the people," he announced. "They have made him king in Hebron. His men will come and kill you if you do not escape."

At once the palace was in an uproar, and in an hour David and those who were loyal to him were fleeing toward the Jordan, then across the Jordan and into the hills on the other side.

It was a sad time for Israel when the friends of David fought against the friends of Absalom. But David's army was stronger, and Absalom was defeated and killed. When the news was brought to David that Absalom was dead, he had more sorrow over the son whom he had lost than he had joy in the victory that gave him back his kingdom.

When David came again to Jerusalem a happier time began for all Israel. The people said, "King David has grown to be a wiser and a better king through what he has suffered." And even after David had been dead many hundreds of years, the people of Israel looked back to him as the one who came nearest to being the kind of king God wanted for his people.

Before David died, he chose his son Solomon to become king in his place. David also gathered together stone and timber and precious metal for a temple in Jerusalem. He told Solomon: "Keep God's laws and walk in his ways as long as you live, for that is the only way in which the kingdom will prosper. And see that you build in Jerusalem a great and beautiful house for the worship of God."

The finest cedar was in the mountain country of Lebanon, and the best workmen to prepare timber for building were in Tyre. So Solomon sent messengers to the king of Tyre.

"I plan to build a temple for my God," the message read. "Give orders, therefore, to your workmen that they cut cedars of Lebanon for me and bring them to Jerusalem. I will send wheat to pay you for what is done."

Soon the walls of the Temple were rising on the rocky hill north of Solomon's palace. Thousands of men worked at the building. People came from all over the land to see it. Never had there been anything like it in Israel.

Solomon said: "The Egyptians have magnificent temples for their gods. The Temple of our God must be as fine as theirs."

But the prophets of God told the king that it was much more important that he and the people should obey God than that he should make the Temple beautiful with hewn stone and cedar and gold.

One night Solomon dreamed a dream. In the dream God said to him, "Ask me for whatever you wish."

Then Solomon answered: "I have been made king over a great people, and I do not know what to do. Give me, therefore, an understanding heart that I may make right decisions for my people and that I may be able to tell the difference between good and evil."

The answer pleased God and he promised Solomon that his kingdom would have great prosperity if he would remember always to be true to God's ways.

Then Solomon awoke, but he remembered the dream.

When the Temple was finished, Solomon sent an order to the heads of all the tribes of Israel:

"In the seventh month there shall be a feast day in Jerusalem, and the Temple that I have built will be dedicated to the Lord. Let the elders of every tribe come."

Jerusalem was crowded as never before, for not only the elders but many others came. They were amazed at the new stone walls that circled the city, but most of all at the magnificent Temple, which could be seen for miles round about.

Then the priests took the Ark and carried it into the new Temple. They placed it in a room by itself, which they called the Holy of Holies, because to them it would always be the most sacred place of all.

In the Temple court there was a bronze altar, and on it the priests offered sacrifices to show their thankfulness to God.

The court was crowded with people, and King Solomon spoke to them, telling them why he had built the Temple. Then he spread forth his hands toward the heavens and prayed:

"Lord God of Israel, there is no God like thee in heaven above or on earth beneath. Behold the heaven of heavens cannot contain thee, much less this house that I have built! When thy people have done any wrong or are in any trouble and they pray toward this place, hear thou in heaven thy dwelling place and forgive."

But it was not only in Jerusalem that Solomon had fine new buildings. All through the land he built strong cities and put soldiers with chariots and horsemen to guard them. He also went southward to the Red Sea and built ships to sail for him to distant ports and to bring riches from afar.

As the years passed, most people in Israel thought that it was wonderful for Solomon to become so rich and powerful. But there were some, such as the prophets of God, who did not think so.

Solomon had many wives. Some were princesses from Egypt and other lands. Each brought with her to her new home the images that her own people worshiped, that she might set them up in Jerusalem. Also, when Solomon was friendly with the kings of other lands, he built places in Jerusalem where the gods of those kings could be worshiped. The prophets remembered the law which said, "Thou shalt have no other gods before me."

Then, too, Solomon's great buildings and his new cities and his army cost large amounts of money. Therefore he had to lay heavy taxes upon the people. His magnificent palace, with all its beautiful furnishings, needed many servants. The prophets remembered what Samuel had said when he warned them against having a king.

Solomon grew proud of his wealth and proud of his power and proud of his fine buildings, and he forgot God, who had given him all that he had.

4. Few Against Many

THE PRINCES in Jerusalem were proud of Solomon's great new buildings and of his army and his fortresses. They dreamed that one day their country might be nearly as powerful as Egypt.

The merchants in Jerusalem were happy too, for even though they had to pay heavy taxes to Solomon, they became very wealthy. The king's ships on the Red Sea brought gold and sandalwood and precious stones from distant Ophir. The camel trains were always bringing new things to sell from Egypt and Syria and from the land of the Hittites far off in the north. Then, too, whenever Solomon conquered another land, there were slaves to do the hardest work for the Israelites or to be sold for a profit.

But not everyone in the land was proud and happy.

The farmers and the workmen said: "Solomon has taken away our sons for his army, and our daughters are like slaves in his palace and in the palaces of his princes. Every time he fights a battle or builds a new city, we have to pay for it even though we starve."

The leaders of the tribes in the north and beyond the Jordan said: "The king has taken away our freedom. We are no longer his brothers in Israel. We are little better than slaves."

The prophets at Shiloh and in Jerusalem said: "Solomon and his nobles have forgotten God. Their way is not God's way for Israel. What does it matter how wealthy and powerful we are if we cease to be God's people? It would be better for us to lose our wealth and power and be a people obedient to God's will."

The prophets at Shiloh did more than complain. They sent one of their company, Ahijah, to Jerusalem to choose one of Solomon's chief officers, named Jeroboam, to be king over the northern tribes. Ahijah met Jeroboam on a road outside the city. He stripped off the new cloak he was wearing and tore it into twelve pieces. Holding them in his hands, he told Jeroboam to take ten of them.

"Thus saith the Lord," said Ahijah, "I am about to tear the kingdom out of the hand of Solomon and I will give you ten tribes."

Soon Solomon heard what Ahijah had done, and sent men to kill Jeroboam before he could become king in the north. But Jeroboam was warned in time and escaped to Egypt.

The tribes of the north were not sorry when Solomon died. They called a great assembly in Shechem and asked the new king, Rehoboam, who was Solomon's son, to appear before them. The king arrived in great state, with a bodyguard and with many of his advisers. But when he took his place on the throne at the assembly of the tribes, he learned that these men were not afraid of him.

One of the oldest chiefs stood forth boldly and said: "Your father laid heavy burdens on us. If you will lighten those burdens, then we will be loyal to you and serve you."

The king was angry that anyone should speak to him in this way, but he answered, "Go away for three days; then return and I will tell you what I will do."

The king called in the older and more trusted princes to ask them what he should do. They told him that if he would plan how best he could serve these people and would treat them justly, they would be faithful to him forever. Then Rehoboam sent the older men away and called in the young nobles with whom he had grown up. They laughed at what the older men had said.

"Show these northern chieftains that you are a king, Rehoboam," they told him. "Don't let them talk to you as though they were as good as you are. Put them in their place now and you will have no more trouble."

On the third day the elders of the northern tribes came back, and Rehoboam took his place on the throne before them. He looked round at them defiantly and then he spoke:

"My father laid heavy burdens on you, but I will make them heavier. My father used a whip on your backs, but the whippings you will get from me will be like the stings of a scorpion."

At once the assembly was in an uproar. The proud northerners told Rehoboam plainly that they would no longer have him as their king. Jeroboam had already returned from Egypt, and soon they made him king over all the tribes except Judah and Benjamin.

Rehoboam wanted to go to war against the northern tribes and try to win back what he had lost. He called together all the men of Judah. But before they could march northward, one of the prophets in Jerusalem told the king and all the people that God had something to say to them.

"It is not God's will," he said, "for you to fight against your own brothers. Go back to your homes and let there be peace in the land."

And, because the prophet spoke for God, his word had more authority with the people of Judah than the word of the king. From that time the Israelites had two kingdoms, one in the north, called Israel, and the other in the south, called Judah.

There were groups of prophets living together at Shiloh, in Jerusalem, and at other places, who wrote down carefully the story of how God had led the Israelites through the years. People went to them when they found it hard to understand what God wanted them to do. But the prophets were not the only ones who stood out bravely for God's way in Israel and Judah. There were farmers and workmen and even some of the nobles who still worshiped the God of their fathers and wanted more than all else to serve him. It was a sorrow to them that so many, both in Israel and Judah, were no better than the idol worshipers of other nations and did not care about the will of God.

In the Northern Kingdom, Jeroboam, whom Ahijah the prophet had chosen to be king, was a great disappointment to all the prophets. He set up golden calves in the shrines at Beth-el and Dan, and told the people that these were the gods that had led them out of Egypt.

In the south Judah was unhappy under Rehoboam, and still more unhappy when Shishak, king of Egypt, marched into Palestine with an army. He forced Jerusalem to give up many of the treasures of both the palace and the Temple. Some people in Judah remembered what Moses had taught their fathers long before, and knew that they should be different from the Syrians and the Philistines and the Egyptians. But many wanted to do just what they saw others doing. On some of the hilltops in Judah there were shrines for the Canaanite god, called Baal, and large numbers of the people still liked to worship there.

The Northern Kingdom, Israel, was stronger and had greater riches than Judah. There were more people in Israel, and the broad valleys grew better grain and grapes than did the high, rocky hills of Judah. There were larger cities in Israel, and through its valleys passed the trade routes along which the caravans traveled between Egypt and Babylon. But there were also greater evils in Israel than in Judah. Most of the kings were selfish tyrants. It often happened that one of them seized the throne by killing the man who was king before him. The nobles seemed to think only of themselves and of how they could become more rich and powerful. None of them liked to hear the prophets speak out in the name of God concerning truth and right. More people in Israel worshiped Baal than in Judah. The priests of Baal were more popular by far than the prophets and priests of God.

It was a dark day in Israel for the prophets and their followers when Ahab became king. Ahab's father, Omri, had been commander of the army when the people made him king. He bought a great hill in the middle of the land, and on it built his royal city of Samaria. His great stone palace made the people think of the palace of Solomon. Kings of other lands came to visit Omri in Samaria. In honor of these kings, Omri and Ahab set up in the streets of the city the idols that their royal visitors worshiped. It made Israel seem more friendly with other countries.

Ahab's queen was Jezebel, the daughter of the king of Sidon. When she came to Samaria, she brought with her priests of the Baal of Sidon and built shrines for them in Israel. The prophets of God were angry. Queen or not, they told her to her face, she must stop her idol worship.

In Sidon, Jezebel's old home, no one spoke in that way to kings or queens or princesses. The king and his family were masters over all, and none could ask them a reason for what they did. It did not please Jezebel that in Israel so many thought that the word a prophet spoke for God should be obeyed more than the orders of any king.

Jezebel thought she knew a way to change things. She gave a command secretly that every prophet of God in the land should be slain. Then, she thought, the people will see whose word is to be obeyed.

There was, however, in the royal household an

officer named Obadiah. When he learned of the cruel order, he gathered a hundred of the prophets and hid them in a cave. At danger to his own life, he took them bread and water day by day until they could escape to a place of safety.

Elijah was the prophet whom Jezebel and Ahab most feared. His home was in the highlands on the east side of the Jordan. He lived much of the time in the rough, lonely country of the Jordan Valley. It was not easy for the king's men to find him there. He would appear suddenly in one of the cities of Israel, speak his message, and as suddenly be gone.

If a farmer had his land stolen by one of the nobles, he knew that Elijah would help him to gain it back. Often when the merchants in the city were cheating the people, Elijah would appear with a warning that God would punish them. It was always bad news for anyone who did wrong to hear that Elijah was in the city.

One year famine came to Palestine. There were no rains in the plowing season or in the growing season, and the land remained hard and dry. When harvesttime came, there was nothing in the fields to reap. There were many hungry people everywhere.

Elijah went to Ahab, the king, and told him that God was punishing Israel for its unfaithfulness. When Ahab told Jezebel what Elijah had said, she insisted that it was all Elijah's fault. If only the king would get rid of that terrible prophet, there would be better days for Israel!

Ahab sent his men in search of Elijah, not only throughout Israel, but to Judah and Moab and Syria and Tyre. But they did not find Elijah. He was living in a secret place in the Jordan Valley where a little brook called Cherith flowed.

The next year there was again no rain in Palestine, and people were starving. The brook Cherith dried up, and Elijah, traveling by night so that he would not be seen, went northward to the country of Sidon where no one would know him and he would be safe. There a widow let him live in her home and shared with him what little food she and her son had. As long as Elijah was with her, there was always enough food for all of them. She was very grateful to Elijah, for, one time when her son was sick and seemed about to die, Elijah prayed for him and he was restored to health.

In the third year of the famine, Elijah went south into Israel to meet Ahab. He found him making a trip through the land with Obadiah, his chief officer, in search of pasture for the horses and mules and cattle that remained.

Ahab was not pleased to see Elijah.

"Is it you, you troubler of Israel?" he asked.

Elijah answered him at once: "I am not the one who has made trouble for Israel, but you and your father's house. You have disobeyed God's commands and have worshiped Baal instead of God. These things cannot go on. I bid you call an assembly of the people on Mount Carmel. Bring along all your prophets of Baal, and we shall see which God is true."

Ahab did what Elijah asked. He knew that Jezebel would be furious with him for doing it. But Ahab was an Israelite and he could not entirely forget the God of Israel. He loved the easier, more pleasant ways of Jezebel and the religion of Baal, but deep within him a voice said, "Elijah is right."

When the people were gathered on Mount Carmel, Elijah spoke to them.

"How long do you think you can go limping back and forth between the God of Israel and the Baal of Jezebel? Make up your minds what you will do. If the Lord be God, follow him—but if Baal, follow him."

Elijah stood silent, waiting for an answer. But no one dared to speak. The prophet went on:

"I, I alone, am left as a prophet of the Lord." The people all knew that many of the prophets had been killed and the others were in hiding. "But there are here four hundred and fifty prophets of Baal. Let them make ready a bull for sacrifice. I also will make one ready. Then let them call upon the name of their god. I also will call upon the name of my God. And the god who answers by fire, he is God."

The sacrifices were made ready. The prophets of Baal shrieked and danced and cut themselves, crying out, "O Baal, hear us!" But nothing happened.

When the time came for Elijah to offer his sacrifice, he called the people to come nearer, and then he prayed quietly and simply:

"O Lord, God of Abraham, of Isaac, and of Jacob, let it be known today that thou art God in Israel, and that I am thy servant. Turn back the heart of this people to thyself once more."

Then came a blinding flash of lightning. The sacrifice that Elijah was offering was set on fire. From the crowd as with one voice came the cry: "The Lord, he is God! The Lord, he is God!"

The people were ready to do anything for Elijah. When he told them that the prophets of Baal who had killed so many of God's prophets must pay for their crimes, they took every one of them down from Carmel to the River Kishon and put them to death. But killing his enemies did not put an end to Elijah's troubles. Instead, it made them worse.

As soon as Jezebel learned what had happened, Elijah had to flee for his life again. This time he went southward through Judah. At Beer-sheba, in the far south, he left his servant and went alone into the desert. He was so discouraged that he wished he might die. He felt that he could endure no more trouble. But while he was sleeping, an angel of God told him to make ready for a long journey. Already God was planning a new task for him.

Elijah's journey was across the rough wilderness where the Israelites had lived so many years when they came out of Egypt. At last he came to the mountain where long ago Moses had waited for God to speak to him. If God had spoken there to Moses, perhaps he would also speak there to Elijah. Elijah found a cave on the mountainside where he could stay.

Then Elijah waited to see what God's message to him would be. Storms beat upon the mountain, and

rocks went rolling down into the valley with a great roar. An earthquake shook the mountain. The lightning set the woods on fire, and the flames shot up toward the sky. Elijah thought perhaps God meant to speak to him through these things, but God's message was in none of them. Then after the earthquake came a great stillness, and Elijah covered his face, for he knew that God was near.

He cried out, "O God, thy people have broken all the promises they made, and I alone am left as a true prophet!" But God told him that there were still seven thousand in Israel who were faithful to their promises. There was still work for a prophet to do, and he must return at once to his task. He must choose a new king for Israel and also for Syria, and he must find a prophet to take up his work after him.

Then Elijah knew that God's work was never done and that God's work could never fail. Once more Elijah was glad to be a prophet. What did it matter if Jezebel and Ahab tried to kill him! They were fighting, not against Elijah, who could die, but against the Lord God himself, who could not die. They could never win if they were enemies of God.

When Elijah returned to the north, a man from the city of Jezreel came to him with a report that roused his anger.

"King Ahab tried to buy the vineyard of Naboth in Jezreel," the man said, "because it was alongside his palace and he wanted it for a garden. Naboth was not willing to sell, and as a free man in Israel he knew that the king could not force him to do so. When Queen Jezebel saw Ahab's disappointment, she mocked him, asking him if he were still king in Israel. She knew a way to get the land. She had the men of the city make a false accusation against Naboth and then stone him to death. So Ahab is enjoying the vineyard even though Naboth refused to sell."

At once Elijah went to Jezreel and found Ahab in his new vineyard. The prophet's eyes flashed and his voice was stern when he spoke.

"You were a murderer and now you are a thief." There was no one but Elijah who would dare speak such words to the king.

Ahab answered him, "So you have found me again, O my enemy."

Then Elijah told him that, because of his evil deeds, he and all his family would die violent deaths. Ahab grew frightened as he listened to Elijah. When he returned to the palace, he fasted and prayed that he might be forgiven. Ahab was an unhappy king who could never quite make up his mind whether to serve God or Baal.

So the years passed. Kings died and new kings were born in both Israel and Judah. False gods were still worshiped, and most of the people liked to do as other nations did rather than as God commanded them. But always there were prophets and people who listened to the prophets. They knew that whatever happened it was best to worship the God of their fathers and to serve him alone.

5. Amos Speaks Out

Your majesty, I ask only for justice. Prince Jarib has stolen my land, and my family and I have been left to starve."

King Jeroboam looked down from his throne at the rough and poorly clad farmer who had to be held back by the soldiers as he made his plea to the king. The poor fellow seemed almost out of his mind. The king turned to a young prince near him whose clothing and jewels showed his wealth.

"Well, Jarib, what have you to say for yourself?"

Jarib stepped forward toward the throne and bowed as he spoke.

"Your majesty, this man lies. I stole nothing from him. He has been in debt to our family for years. He has had his chance to pay, but he is lazy and worthless—"

"Who can pay his debts when they double each year they are not paid?" the farmer broke in angrily.

"Silence!" shouted Jeroboam. "How dare you interrupt when a prince is speaking? Proceed with your evidence, Jarib."

"As I was saying, the debt has been unpaid for years," the prince continued. "At last I had no more patience and took the man's land as part payment. He should be grateful that I did not sell him and his family as slaves to pay the remainder of the debt."

The king said nothing for a moment. There was no sound but the gentle swish of the great palm-leaf fans. When at last he spoke, his voice was hard.

"We have too many of these lazy farmers complaining about injustice. Let this fellow receive twenty lashes; then turn him loose."

The farmer was led away, shouting as he went that he had been wronged. Prince Jarib expressed his gratitude to the king, and then hurried away to see that the sentence was properly carried out. The king leaned back in his seat and enjoyed the breeze from the fans as he waited for what would come next.

Through a narrow window he could look out across the valley. Beyond it were other hills and valleys. All of them were his. It was good to be king over Israel in such prosperous days.

Jeroboam thought of his grandfather's time, when war with the king of Syria left the Israelites with only fifty horsemen and ten chariots. Much of the country was made desolate. Then he thought of his father's time when Syria fell before an enemy from farther north and the Israelites had a chance to gain back their land and their cities. Now Jeroboam was king over a land nearly as great as when David was king.

Often Jeroboam feared that the northern warriors who had conquered Syria might march southward against Israel. He sent them a gift to make his peace with them but he knew they might want more than a gift. They were cruel and greedy, and they were always wanting to make some new land a part of their empire. But so far all had gone well and Jeroboam was content. Who could wish for more than he had—wealth, comfort, pleasures, and princes who were always ready to do his bidding?

An officer of the court interrupted Jeroboam's thoughts: "Your majesty, the prophet for whom you sent has come."

The king turned his head to find before him a plain-looking man.

"I want to know," the king began abruptly, "is it safe for me to journey to Megiddo tomorrow?"

"Let music be brought, and you shall have your answer," said the prophet.

A musician was quickly brought in, and as he played softly the prophet began to sway gently to and fro. At first his eyes were closed; then they opened; but he seemed to see no one. Suddenly the music stopped, and in the stillness the prophet's voice sounded clearly.

"The Lord says to Jeroboam, king of Israel, that he will be safe. Because Jeroboam honors the prophets of the Lord and delights in making great offerings in the shrine at Beth-el, the Lord will be with him all his days and bless him in all that he does."

Jeroboam looked pleased and ordered his treasurer to give the prophet a gift as he went out. He turned to an aged prince who stood by him.

"It is pleasant to have good words from a prophet," he said. "I would not like to have a prophet like Elijah coming in here and telling me what to do. But after all, in those days the kings of Israel murdered the prophets of God instead of taking care of them as we do."

The prince bowed low and answered: "There can be no doubt, my king, that the God of Israel looks with favor on us. Who knows what great things he may yet do for us?"

The road southward from Samaria had many trav-

elers on it, for it was festival time at the royal sanctuary in Beth-el. Most of the people traveled the twen-
ty-five miles on foot, but often they had to step off the
road to let some nobleman pass in his chariot.

Crowds packed the narrow streets, and every house
had as many people in it as it would hold. The voices
of merchants, shouting their wares or arguing over
the price with a buyer, could be heard on every side.
Hungry beggars looked longingly at the food offered
for sale or whined to the passers-by for a little gift.

In the shrine, sacrifices were being offered constantly and the music of the sacred services was heard again and again. Priests hurried to and fro. As soon as one banquet ended, another began.

Few of the people noticed a strong, sharp-eyed farmer who took his stand near the Temple gate. He looked like any other farmer who had come to town to trade and to take part in the festival. He watched the gay crowd surging by him for a time. Some who had just finished feasting in the Temple staggered drunkenly by. Priests went past who were as drunk as the worst of them.

The farmer motioned to the people to gather round him and began to speak:

"The Lord God showed me a vision, and I saw him forming grasshoppers to eat up everything that grows. When they had finished eating the grass, I cried out, 'O Lord God, forgive Israel, for it is small.' Then the grasshoppers passed away.

"But there came another vision. The Lord was sending forth fire to test his people. It devoured the great deep and was about to devour the plowland. I cried out, 'O Lord God, turn back the fire, for Israel is small.' And the fire turned back."

The crowd had become quiet as they listened. More and more people had gathered round. The man spoke slowly so that every word could be heard. He knew that the people were pleased that in his visions God's judgment was twice turned away from them. Were they not God's people? No harm could come to them.

The voice went on with quickening speed:

"Then came a third vision. I saw the Lord standing upon a wall with a plumb line in his hand. The Lord said to me, 'Amos, what do you see?' and I said, 'A plumb line to measure the straightness of a wall.' And the Lord said: 'I am measuring my people Israel with this plumb line. Because they are like a wall that is crooked, I will bring judgment upon them. Their shrines on the hilltops will be laid waste and their buildings broken down. And the house of King Jeroboam will perish by the sword.'"

The people were no longer pleased. Some were angry, and called out that it was treason to say such things about the royal shrine and the king. Some were frightened, and moved away quickly lest there should be trouble. A half-drunken noble who had heard the last words sent his servant running back into the Temple to bring the royal priest. But there were some people, farmers and workmen and ragged beggars, who gathered about the speaker and wanted to hear more from him.

Soon Amaziah, the royal priest, came hurrying through the crowd. He stopped in front of Amos.

"What does this mean? You cannot talk treason here at the royal sanctuary or anywhere else!" he roared at the prophet.

"I talk not treason, but truth," Amos answered in a calm voice.

"I know you fellows," Amaziah went on. "You like to frighten people, and then they pay you well to change your bad news into good news. You are from Judah, I see. Then away with you, back to Judah where you belong! Do your prophesying there and earn your bread. But never again come to Beth-el to prophesy, for this is the king's sanctuary and the king's palace."

Amos showed no fear, but answered boldly.

"I am not one of the prophets whose words can be bought and sold. I do not belong among those who are trained to be prophets. I am a shepherd from Tekoa. When I was tending my flock, God said to me, 'Go, preach to my people Israel.' So now I have something to say to you. Because you have told me not to speak the truth to this people, great troubles shall yet come upon you and your family, and you will see the day when this people is carried away into exile in a foreign land."

In spite of Amaziah's warning, Amos did not leave Beth-el immediately. He had been given work to do, and he would remain until he had finished it.

Some days he wandered through the streets, watching the crowds bearing gifts to the shrine or listening to men buying and selling in the market place. It made him angry to see the many ways in which the merchants cheated the poor people who were afraid to complain. Sometimes they used false measures, or cheated in the amount given in making an exchange of coins. More than once he saw a judge give his decision against a workman because someone paid him a bribe. Servants from the palaces of the nobles came to him and told him that their masters and their wives feasted and drank wine all day long. Yet these same masters counted on God to be good to them because they offered such fine sacrifices.

The more Amos saw and heard, the more he had to speak. He was sure that the people who had forgotten their God so completely and given themselves up to such evil and selfish ways must soon meet with a great disaster. It was his duty to warn them before it was too late. But most of them did not want to be warned.

One day Amos spoke to some noble women from Samaria. They were dressed in the finest of silks. They were loaded down with jewels. And they were very fat from all their eating and drinking. The sight of them made Amos think of the fat cows he had seen in the country of Bashan across the Jordan.

The prophet stood before them, and when he spoke,
his words shocked them:

"Hear this word, you cows of Bashan, who make
your homes in the mountains of Samaria. You oppress
the weak; you crush the needy. The only thing you
know how to do is to call to your husbands, 'Bring us
more wine to drink!' The Lord God is bringing days
upon you when enemies will drag you through the
broken walls of your city."

Another day Amos stood again at the gate of the
shrine and the crowd was greater than before.

"Hear what God is saying to you," he cried. "He
says: 'I hate your feasts, and you cannot please me
with all your sacrifices. Take away from me the noise
of your songs and your musicians. Let justice roll
down like waters and righteousness like a mighty
river. Let every man do what is just and right and
merciful, or I will destroy you utterly.'"

So angry was Amaziah when he heard what Amos
had said about the services in the shrine that he sent
officers to arrest him. But Amos was gone. He had
given his warning, and now he was on the road back
to his beloved hills at Tekoa.

But that was not the last visit Amos made to Bethel. More than once he left his flock and suddenly appeared with his startling warnings among the crowds at the royal shrine. There were always some who were glad to hear him. They believed, as he did, that unless Israel changed its ways the nation would soon be destroyed. But most of the people thought his talk was nonsense and hardly worth listening to.

King Jeroboam received a report from the priest Amaziah about Amos.

"I would not be surprised," Amaziah wrote, "if this mad prophet were planning a conspiracy against you and against your throne. He has even dared to say that you will be slain."

Jeroboam, however, was so sure of his power and success that he did nothing against Amos. He was not wise enough to know that it would be better for his kingdom if he listened to Amos rather than to the princes and prophets who told him what he liked to hear.

When Jeroboam died, Israel had three kings in one year. There seemed to be few wise leaders left. Then Tiglath-pileser came marching into the land with his Assyrian army, and the Israelites could not stand against him. The farmers and the poor people in the cities did not care what happened. They thought that nothing could make them unhappier than they were.

Tiglath-pileser made the king of Israel pay a fine of one thousand talents of silver and promise that he would never revolt against the Assyrian king, but would be his loyal subject. Then he marched away, leaving Israel almost in ruins. He took with him to Assyria, as prisoners, many of the people of the land.

What the prophets had said was true. They had warned the king and the people of Israel that, if they continued to reject God's word and to disobey his laws, the nation would be destroyed. But hardly anyone would listen. So the day was almost at hand when the Kingdom of Israel would come to an end.

6. Turn Ye!

WHEN Isaiah was a boy, he thought Jerusalem the most wonderful place in all the world. He often climbed to the top of the great wall near his father's house and walked along it, looking out at the hills on every side. He could look down into the city from the wall and watch what people were doing. Away across the city he saw the roof and towers of the king's palace and, higher still, the Temple.

He liked to go across the city, out through the eastern gate, and down into the valley of the Kidron. It was *so* far down to the bottom of the valley! When he looked upward the walls and towers high above seemed almost to touch the sky. Surely no enemy could ever climb that hill and then scale the wall!

Isaiah was proud of his city and proud of his king. Isaiah's father said that Uzziah had been king in Judah as long as he could remember. When there was a royal procession, the whole family watched from the house-top, and it was exciting to hear the crowds shouting, "Long live the king!" and then, when the king came in sight, to join in the shout. They were all sad the day it was reported that King Uzziah had leprosy and could never again appear among his people.

In school the priest, who was the teacher, told the boys stories of what had happened long ago in Judah. As he talked or read from a scroll, they could imagine they saw Abraham wandering across these hills that they knew so well, or Joshua coming up from the Jordan Valley and capturing one city after another. Best of all they liked the stories of David and his many adventures. Isaiah never tired of hearing how God had been leading his people through the years. No other nation could say what *they* could say—that they were God's own people. That was what made him proudest to be a son of Judah.

There were older boys who had been to Egypt and Assyria. They could talk of nothing but the magnificent temples and palaces and the great armies they had seen. When they returned from their travels, everything in Jerusalem seemed to them poor and hardly worth looking at. Judah was so small and had such a little army. They wished they were Egyptians or Assyrians. That would be something worth-while! But, no matter what they said, Isaiah went on being glad he belonged to Judah.

Isaiah was still a young man when he first heard about Amos. A friend of his father's had been at Beth-el for the festival and came to tell him what had happened.

"A crazy fellow from down here in Tekoa," he said, "was jabbering about God refusing any longer to be our God. He accused the princes and the merchants of cheating the people. He even threatened the king. Most of the prophets are afraid that he will only cause trouble talking like that. All the riffraff in the country are ready to follow a preacher who says such things."

Isaiah said nothing, but he searched through Jerusalem until he found someone who had brought back from Beth-el a written copy of many of the words of Amos. What he read thrilled him. No one he knew ever talked as Amos did. Even the best prophets and priests in Jerusalem were careful not to make anyone angry. But Amos cared so much about God that he did not care if people became angry or what might happen to him.

A few years later, word came to Jerusalem of another prophet in the north. His name was Hosea. Like Amos, he warned the Israelites that they were sure to have trouble unless they changed their ways. He was just as brave as Amos, but he was different. When Hosea spoke, it was as though God himself was pleading with his people to turn back to him before it was too late.

One day Isaiah went up to the Temple to worship. He could not remember when first he had watched the smoke curling upward from the altar. The songs of the Temple choir had been part of his life since he was a boy. But this day he did not see or hear much of what was going on around him.

Suddenly it seemed to him as though the presence of God himself was filling all the Temple. God was very near to him. It was as though he had never known before who God was. God was so great, so holy, so pure, and Isaiah felt so small and weak and sinful. Isaiah had always thought of God as Judah's God and Israel's God. Now he understood what Amos meant when he said that the Lord was ruler over the whole earth. Not only Judah and Israel, but Egypt, and Assyria, and all the nations belonged to him.

One thing Isaiah knew well—the people of Jerusalem were far away from God in all that they were doing. They did not know the truth about God at all. His heart sank within him as he thought how wrong were the things he himself had been doing. Surely God would have nothing to do with such disobedient people! Then he heard God saying to him, "I have forgiven you," and it was as though a great weight were being lifted from him.

But what of the people of Judah? Was there no hope for them? If they would repent, God would forgive them. But how could they repent unless someone would go to them and speak to them in God's name?

A voice sounded in Isaiah's ears: "Who will go and be a prophet to my people?"

At once Isaiah knew that God was calling him to go. He could hardly believe it. He had never thought, when he had heard of Amos and Hosea, that he might become a prophet one day too. But now he answered at once,

"Here am I; send me."

Isaiah found that it was hard to keep the promise he had made in the Temple. He had always known that the judges were dishonest and that some of the princes would have men murdered who stood against their plans. But now he had to go into the open square and tell the whole city that God would surely punish these men for what they were doing.

All over the city were places where people worshiped idols, and evil things were done in the shrines of the idols. Isaiah had never paid much attention to them before. Now he stood in the street in front of these shrines and warned the people that they were giving up their own true God when they went to worship there.

Isaiah spoke also to the king, for the king had more power to do right or to do wrong than anyone else.

The king sometimes listened patiently to Isaiah, but at other times he was angry.

From far in the north reports came to Jerusalem that made everyone afraid. It was not long since Tiglath-pileser and his Assyrian armies had marched

down into Palestine. What if one day he took Israel and then came south into Judah? Every day in the market place and in the streets men were asking, "What is Assyria going to do next?"

When they asked Isaiah, he said: "Israel and Judah can expect great trouble. God is sending the Assyrians against us to punish us because we have been so unfaithful to him. They will destroy our cities and take our people away. Only a few will be left. But if those who remain will turn back to God he will do great things for them."

Isaiah wanted the people to remember his words. So when a son was born in his home he gave him the name Shearjashub, which meant "Only a Remnant Shall Return." Every time anyone called out the name of the boy it made the people think of what the prophet had said.

It was not Assyria that first came marching against Judah, but its northern neighbors Israel and Syria. The kings of these countries wanted Judah to join in an alliance with them and defy the king of Assyria. The king of Judah refused, and the other two decided to make war on him. When word reached Jerusalem, King Ahaz was terrified. He sent men to inspect all the walls and gates, and he himself went to make sure that the water supply was in good condition.

While Ahaz was standing by the upper pool, he saw Isaiah coming toward him with his little son by the hand. He wondered what the prophet would have to say to him now. He had no time to listen to a prophet when the city was in danger. He thought he must get back to the palace and send a message to Tiglath-pileser. That was it! Ask the Assyrian to come and help him against these enemies! It would serve them right.

The prophet and the boy had reached him now. Ahaz remembered the strange name of the boy — Shearjashub, "A Remnant Shall Return." That did not make the king feel any happier or more comfortable.

"Take heed, O king," said Isaiah, "and be calm. Don't be so frightened of these kings from the north. And don't go looking for help from some foreign king. What you need most of all is to trust in God. If you refuse to put your trust in him, your kingdom will never be strong."

"You talk about trusting God, Isaiah," said the king, "but what we need is an army to drive our enemies back, and I think I know where I can find one!"

"Yes," answered Isaiah, "you can send for the Assyrians, and perhaps when they have beaten Syria and Israel, they will come farther south and take Judah too!"

The king paid no heed to Isaiah but returned to the palace. People were streaming into Jerusalem from all the villages round about, carrying with them whatever they wanted to save from the enemy. At last the gates were closed and barred. Jerusalem was ready for the siege.

When Isaiah heard that the king was gathering together all the gold and silver in the palace and the Temple, he knew that Ahaz was not doing as he had advised him. Ahaz was preparing a gift for the king of Assyria. The gift was sent, and soon an Assyrian army was marching on Damascus, drawing away both the Syrians and the Israelites from their siege of Jerusalem.

When Tiglath-pileser had conquered Damascus, Ahaz journeyed north to see his parade of victory. When he returned, he could talk of nothing but the wonderful doings of the Assyrians. He had brought back the plan of an Assyrian altar which he admired, and he had one exactly like it built for the Temple in Jerusalem. Isaiah was not happy when he saw what was happening. Many people thought Ahaz had won a great victory, but Isaiah knew that what he was doing could lead only to ruin.

Ten years later the people of Judah saw what a mistake Ahaz had made. The Assyrians invaded Israel again and carried away most of its people to distant parts of their empire. Some of the people fled to Judah and made their homes there. Many of the poorest remained in the north and lived alongside the new settlers, who came with strange languages and strange ways. Judah, high up on its hills, a very little nation, was left to carry on alone as the people of God. Never again was there a Kingdom of Israel!

There were many who remembered what Amos and

Hosea had said. The prophets had been right, even though nearly everyone made fun of them. Israel had not changed its ways, so disaster had come. That made some in Judah more willing to listen to Isaiah and more anxious about what would happen to Jerusalem unless the people returned soon to God's ways.

Isaiah was not alone in his work. There were many who would have nothing to do with him, but there were others whose lives had been made stronger and better by listening to his words. They went with him when he had a message to declare in the Temple court or in the market place. Sometimes they wrote down what he said. Often they sat in his house, talking with him about the things that were happening and trying to understand what God wanted them to do.

Hezekiah, the son of King Ahaz, had friends who were followers of Isaiah, and he knew what Isaiah was teaching. When he became king, he gave orders that the people should no longer worship at the little shrines all over the country, but should come to the Temple in Jerusalem to worship. He thought that this would put an end to the evil things that were done in the shrines. In the Temple in Jerusalem he took away the altars where men worshiped foreign gods and told them they must worship only the God of their fathers. This made many people angry. They thought Judah would be wealthy and successful if they worshiped the gods of the Egyptians and the Assyrians as well as their own God.

After some years another Assyrian king, Sennacherib, came marching into Palestine with his army, capturing the cities of the Philistines on the coast and then moving up into the hills of Judah. None of the cities, except Jerusalem, was strong enough to resist him. He carried away thousands of the people and left many of the cities in ruins. There was little food left in Judah, because the Assyrian soldiers had eaten it or taken it away.

In Jerusalem, Isaiah spoke to the people, who were no longer proud, but frightened and hopeless.

"God is saying something to us through these days of trouble. Hear what God says: 'I brought you up as my children and my people, but you refused to obey me. An ox knows enough to return to his master's stable, and a donkey always comes back to the place where it is fed, but my people do not understand as well as an ox or a donkey; they do not know that I am their Father and that they are my family. They make themselves unhappy with their evil ways. Change your ways now; return to me with all your heart; then perhaps better days will come for Judah.'"

The priests said that if only greater sacrifices were offered on the altars in the Temple, God would be kinder to Judah, and things would go better. The people were glad to do what the priests said, because it was easier to give costly gifts than to change their ways. Isaiah did not agree with them, and he told them so.

"God says to you that he has no pleasure in all your rich offerings as long as you disobey him in your lives," he told them plainly. "It will do you no good to crowd into the Temple courts and to hold a multitude of services if you go on doing evil. Do what is just and right and see to it that no one is oppressed. Do not cheat when you do business. Take care of children whose fathers and mothers have died. That is the kind of thing God wants you to do."

When the people asked Isaiah about the Assyrians, he said to them: "God sent the Assyrians against us because we have been so unfaithful to his ways. But God will keep us from being entirely destroyed or all carried away. The Assyrians are so powerful that they think they are greater than God himself. Someday they too will fall. When that day comes there will still be a few of our people who are faithful to God and who obey his ways."

After Hezekiah and Isaiah had died, there came a time when all the followers of Isaiah had to suffer for their faith. Hezekiah's son, Manasseh, built up the old shrines on the hilltops and brought back the worship of foreign gods in Jerusalem. Whoever spoke against what he was doing was put to death. But, no matter what he did, he could not stop people from thinking that Isaiah had been right. They gathered in little groups in their homes to read what Isaiah had said and to pray for better days to come.

7. No Escape

ONE SUNNY afternoon a boy ran to the top of a hill outside Anathoth and looked down the road toward Jerusalem. Surely his father would be coming soon! If only he could have gone to Jerusalem too! Such exciting things were happening there. Josiah was being made king. Some of the princes did not want Josiah to be king and there might be serious trouble.

The boy went slowly back to his house. He said to his mother: "Josiah is only eight years old. Will he really be a king?"

"Just wait until your father returns, Jeremiah," she answered, "and he will tell you all about Josiah."

When at last his father came, Jeremiah had to hear all that had happened—whether Josiah was frightened, and what kind of crown the priest put on his head, and how many people were there, and whether Josiah would still have to go to school now that he was king.

His father answered each question patiently, for he was glad that Jeremiah was interested in the young king. Long years before, King Manasseh had been angry with their family and other people who did not want him to build altars to foreign gods. Many of them had been killed or driven from Jerusalem.

But now it was all changed. The friends of the young king Josiah were good men, men who trusted God, and they would help him to rule well.

From that day Jeremiah was able to go into Jerusalem often, and soon he knew the city as well as he knew his own village of Anathoth.

At home Jeremiah's father was teaching him to become a priest of God, as his father and his grandfather had been. He had to learn all the laws about the sacrifices and the sacred rules which the people were supposed to follow. But what he liked better was to hear the story of how God had brought Israel out of Egypt and all that he had done for them since that time. Israel's God was so different from the gods of the Egyptians and the Assyrians and the Philistines. No other nation had ever known a God like him. Other gods were cruel and unjust, but Israel's God loved justice and hated everything that was cruel and wrong. Jeremiah was glad to think that he would be a priest of so wonderful a God.

But it was not as a priest that Jeremiah was to serve God.

When he grew to be a young man, he saw that there were not many people in Jerusalem or in any of the cities of Judah who cared as he did about God. All around Jerusalem were shrines where men set up idols and worshiped them. Men wanted most of all to become wealthy; they did not want to hear about the will of God. The walls of the Temple were falling down because they had not been repaired for many years. In the markets men cheated and lied, without even thinking they were doing wrong.

But what surprised Jeremiah was that none of the prophets ever told the people that they were disobeying God. When the prophets spoke, they said that God was with the people in Jerusalem and all would be well. Jeremiah said to himself, "Even these prophets, who should speak for God, have forgotten him and do not know him any longer."

Jeremiah knew that God hated injustice and stealing and untruthfulness and the worship of idols. He knew also that if the people of Jerusalem continued to do what God hated, they would soon be destroyed, as Samaria had been one hundred years before.

Because Jeremiah knew these things, he had to speak out and warn his people. It seemed to him that from his very birth God had been preparing him to be a prophet. He knew how hard it would be. What would all the older men say when he stood up in the court of the Temple and called upon them to change their ways and return to God? Already he could hear some of them laughing and saying: "Why should we listen to this young fool? He is hardly more than a child."

Jeremiah said to God, "I am too young and I do not know how to speak to these people."

God answered him: "Do not say you are too young. Go where I send you and speak what I command you. Have no fear of anyone. I will be with you to teach you what you should say."

"Hear ye the word of the Lord, O house of Jacob." The words rang out across the Temple court, and all the people who were moving toward the gate stopped. Jeremiah had been frightened, but as he began to speak, he gained confidence. He thought only of winning these people back to God. He went on speaking:

"Thus saith the Lord, Have I wronged you that you have turned away from me and serve other gods? I brought you out of Egypt and led you into this land of plenty. But when you were settled in it you refused to be my people and obey my voice. Have any other nations done what you have done? Their gods are false gods, yet they remain loyal to them. But you have forsaken me and have made for yourselves idols which cannot help you.

"Hear now God's warning: If you reject him, then he will reject you and cast you off from being his people."

As Jeremiah stopped speaking, there was a hush for a moment and then a dozen people spoke at once.

"It's Jeremiah, Hilkiah's son, from Anathoth. Since when did he become a prophet?"

"Why should we listen to this boy?"

"I would rather hear the other prophets than this fellow."

But there were a few men who came to him afterward and told him they knew that what he said was true. They had been wishing for a long time for someone who would speak plainly for God as he did.

Five years after Jeremiah became a prophet, a great discovery was made in the Temple. Josiah had given orders that the Temple was to be repaired. Some walls had to be torn down and rebuilt. Many rooms had to have new roofs made for them. Workmen were busy everywhere. In a room that had not been open for many years, one of the workmen found a large scroll. He did not know what it was, but he took it to the priest, who saw at once that on it were written the laws of God. It had been written long ago when men understood God's law much better than they did in these days of King Josiah.

Shaphan, the king's secretary, was sent to show the book to the king.

At the king's command Shaphan opened it and began to read:

" 'Give ear, ye heavens, and I will speak;
    And let the earth hear the words of my mouth. . . .
    For I will proclaim the name of the Lord:
    Ascribe ye greatness unto our God. . . .
    For all his ways are justice:
    A God of faithfulness and without iniquity,
    Just and right is he.
    The people have dealt corruptly with him,
    They are not his children, . . .
    They are a perverse and crooked generation.' "

The king leaned forward, listening carefully.

"Read on," he commanded Shaphan.

As Shaphan read, the king's face became thoughtful and anxious. When the reading was finished, he cried out to all the people about him:

"These words are true. They tell us what God asks of us. But we have not done what he asks. Perhaps it is not too late for us to change our ways."

The king sent messengers at once to every city in Judah, commanding the elders to come to Jerusalem. They gathered in one of the courts of the Temple, and Shaphan read to them all that was in the Book of the Law. Then the king and the people promised that they would keep the Commandments and be faithful to the covenant which their fathers had made with God in the days of Moses.

It was an unhappy day in Judah for everyone who made money from the worship of idols. The king sent men to break down the altars and destroy the idols. Anyone who still worshiped them was punished. The king of Judah also commanded that from this day on all the people were to go to Jerusalem to worship God.

There were many people in Judah who soon forgot what they had heard from the Book of the Law, and forgot the promises they had made. They went back to their old ways and were as cruel and dishonest as they had been before. Some of the priests and prophets still talked of the book that had been found. But even they forgot to do the things that were commanded in the book.

In his own village, Jeremiah heard men saying, "God will be with us now, and we shall have peace because the king and all the people have accepted God's law." Even Jeremiah's friends thought that a new day had come in Judah because the Book of the Law had been discovered.

Jeremiah said to them: "Do you think that you are wise and good because you have God's law in a book? The law will do you no good unless you do what it says. God asks you to worship him alone, but you still worship other gods. God asks you to be honest, but you cheat each other every day. God asks you to speak truth, but everywhere I hear lies. If you go on like this, God will destroy Jerusalem and it won't make any difference that you have the Book of the Law."

Neither in Anathoth nor in Jerusalem did men like to hear this. They hated Jeremiah because he told them that they spoke one thing but did the opposite. They did everything they could to make him stop speaking.

None of them knew how nearly they succeeded. Jeremiah felt that he could not go on living if everyone hated him and tried to do him harm. He said to himself, "I will no longer speak God's word to the people if they do not want to hear it." Just as he had one day decided to be God's prophet, so now he would choose to give it up.

Then Jeremiah discovered that being God's spokesman was not something he could give up when he pleased. When he tried to keep from speaking the truth, it made him unhappier than when he spoke it. God's word was like a fire burning inside him, and he could not keep it in. He could not watch his people take the wrong path and not try to show them the right path. He had to do what God wanted him to do, even though his best friends turned against him.

Many years passed. Egypt wanted to rule Palestine and Syria, so the Pharaoh marched northward with his armies. When King Josiah went out against him with his little army, he was defeated and killed. Far to the east, Babylonia was becoming a great empire. Pharaoh, as he marched farther north, met the Babylonian army and was driven back to Egypt.

While these things were happening, Jeremiah kept telling all the people in Judah that unless they turned back to God with their whole heart, the king of Babylon would come and carry them away into captivity. Perhaps if they had to endure some great suffering, it would bring them to their senses and make them more willing to obey God.

At last Jeremiah's words came true. The king of Babylon sent his army against Jerusalem, and, when he had captured it, took the king and princes and priests and workmen with their families to live in a distant part of his empire. Thousands of people had to leave their homes and go into exile. The Babylonians appointed a new king in Judah named Zedekiah, and made him promise to do what they said. Each year he was to collect heavy taxes from the people of Judah and send the money to Babylon.

After a time Zedekiah said to his nobles, "It would be better for us to ask Egypt to help us so that we should no longer have to pay tribute to Babylon." He sent men to talk to the Pharaoh.

When Jeremiah heard what had been done, he went to the palace and told the king and the princes that they had lost their senses. They would get no real help from the Egyptians, and they would only bring upon themselves the anger of Nebuchadnezzar, the king of Babylon. It would be far better to submit to Babylon and to set their minds upon how they could become more truly the people of God.

Some of the nobles said: "Jeremiah is a traitor. His words weaken the people's willingness to fight. He tells them that it is God's will for them to give in to the Babylonians. Lock him up in jail! Put him to death!"

From that day Jeremiah had to suffer greatly. One of the priests had him locked in the public stocks for saying that the Temple would be destroyed. All who passed by in the streets laughed at him as he sat there with his head and his hands and his feet through holes in the boards. Then the king put him in prison, and would have killed him if Shaphan's son had not pleaded for him. When the Babylonians were besieging the city, he was put in a deep dungeon which had soft mud in it, but an Ethiopian servant of the king rescued him and cared for him. This man had heard Jeremiah speak in the palace and he respected him more than he did anyone else in Jerusalem.

But nothing could save Jerusalem now. The Kingdom of Judah was almost at an end. After a two-year siege Jerusalem fell to the Babylonians. The king and many of the people tried to escape, but they were caught. The Babylonians were kind to Jeremiah, taking him from prison and sending him home in safety, but thousands were carried away into exile. The walls of Jerusalem, the Temple, and most of the houses were broken down or burned. Only farmers and shepherds were left in Judah, and everyone was very poor.

Jeremiah told the people who were left not to despair, but to trust God. Now a new and better nation could begin to grow. God had to tear down what had been wrongly built before he could make them the people he wanted them to be.

The men and women who had been carried off to Babylon were planning all the time how they could get back to Judah. Jeremiah wrote them a letter they did not like. It said:

"God's word to you is that you should build homes and plant gardens in Babylon. Seek to live peacefully in the city to which you have been carried. Believe no prophet who says that you will soon return to Judah, for your stay there will be long. Rather, God says to you, 'You shall seek me and find me when you search for me with all your heart; then will I gather you from all the lands and bring you back to your own land.' "

To those in Jerusalem, Jeremiah talked of a day when God would make a new covenant with his people and give them a new heart so that they would love him and serve him. He pleaded with them to stay in Judah and rebuild their nation on God's plan. But Jeremiah was disappointed again. The leader and many of the people, in fear of the Babylonians, fled to Egypt for safety. They made Jeremiah go with them, and soon after arriving in Egypt, he died.

It seemed as though everything Jeremiah had tried to do had failed. But not everyone forgot what he had said. There were many who remembered how he remained faithful to God no matter what men said or did to him. His disciple, Baruch, had written down his words. When men read them, whether it was in Babylon, in Egypt, or in Palestine, they said: "It was Jeremiah who had eyes to see, and we were blind. Jeremiah is dead, but the word which he spoke for God will live. It is time for us to listen and obey."

8. Only One Hope

ELEVEN years before Jeremiah saw Jerusalem destroyed, lines of weary prisoners were moving slowly across the country toward Babylon. It was hot and dry on the desert road. There were hills ahead, but beyond the hills would be more desert. Would this journey never be ended? Hundreds of miles on foot! But the Babylonian soldiers had not been cruel; they had not made them travel too fast.

Simeon's feet were sore, and his whole body was so tired that he wondered how he could go on. But he *must* go on. And his wife Abigail and the boys! What if one of them should be sick? Simeon shuddered as he remembered all the times that sick people had been left beside the road. The Babylonians could not let a thousand prisoners stop on this long journey just because someone was sick and couldn't walk.

Simeon looked ahead. As far as he could see, men and women were stumbling along, each with a bundle of belongings that he had been able to gather together at the last minute. The soldiers rode alongside, keeping everyone in order.

123

Simeon knew this was just one of many caravans that were slowly moving toward Babylon. He remembered how he had turned for a last time and looked back at the walls of Jerusalem. He was glad the city and the Temple had not been destroyed—not this time at least. He could still see them in his mind, and it was like a great weight upon his heart that he would never look on them again. The Babylonian soldiers kept telling the travelers that they would have better homes than ever before in the land to which they were going. But it would not be like Jerusalem! He wished they had let him stay in Judah!

In Tel-abib everyone was busy. It was some weeks now since the first weary exiles arrived from Palestine. There were houses to be built of mud blocks and furniture to be made. The potters were hard at work making dishes for food and jars for water and grain. Gardens had been planted, and already the green shoots were several inches high. The people did not have to wait for rain to come, as they always did in Palestine, for they could draw water out of the canal that ran past their fields.

"Perhaps living here will not be too bad," Simeon thought, as he came from the field in the evening. Then he caught sight of a soldier standing guard beyond the last house, and he changed his mind. "Slaves! That's what we shall be here, just like our forefathers in Egypt. We shall never be free again."

That night when Simeon took his place among the elders in the house of Nethaniah, the talk was of Jerusalem. What would be happening there now? How long would it be until they could go back? Perhaps some country would conquer Babylon and let the prisoners go. Or it might be that a few men could escape and reach Jerusalem safely.

Suddenly one of the elders who had said nothing broke in: "I think all of you are wrong. What Jeremiah said was true. Our troubles have come upon us because we broke our promises to God and refused to repent of our sins. It is God who has brought us to this foreign land, and he will leave us here until we learn to trust him and to obey him as children obey their father."

"Jeremiah was a traitor!" cried out another of the elders. "He spoke against his own city and his own people. The less we hear of Jeremiah's God, the better it will be for us. Nebuchadnezzar worships Marduk, and see what power he has. Perhaps it would do no harm for us to worship Marduk too."

Some agreed with the one speaker and some with the other, and the argument went on for hours. When at last Simeon went back to Abigail and his two boys, he hardly knew what to think.

Month after month and year after year went by until Simeon had been five years in Tel-abib. There was more food for everyone now, and the houses were

more comfortable. But most of the people thought that soon they would be going back to Jerusalem. They seemed to be able to think of nothing else.

One evening when the elders went to the house of Nethaniah, they found a stranger there. Nethaniah introduced him to them as they came in. His name was Ezekiel. He sat silent both that night and the following nights, listening to all that the elders had to say. On the seventh night he rose and spoke to them.

"Men of Judah, God has called me to be a watchman over his people and to warn them when they fall into wickedness that they may turn from their wicked ways and live. When I came among you a week ago, my spirit was angry and bitter because I had seen how little our people have changed their ways. They have idols in their houses and they do evil continually. Surely God's anger must be against us still. But as I have sat among you these days, the anger and the bitterness have passed from me. God has sent me to care for you and to watch over you that you may learn his ways."

Some of the elders did not like it when Ezekiel warned them that a still greater disaster would come upon Jerusalem. They could not deny that altars to Egyptian and Assyrian gods had been built in the Temple itself. Nor could they say anything when he made the accusation that neither they nor their friends in Jerusalem had as yet shown any signs of true repentance.

Simeon was glad that Ezekiel had come to Tel-abib. Now in the evenings when the discussions began, everyone turned to the prophet to hear what he would say. Sometimes when he tried to tell them about God they found it hard to understand him.

There were two things he made clear: that wickedness always leads to pain and trouble, and that God is a help to everyone who really trusts him and serves him.

The unhappiest day Simeon ever knew was the day news came to Tel-abib about the destruction of Jerusalem. At first the people could not believe that it was true: the great stones from the walls lying in heaps, the Temple burned, the houses in ruins. But when they knew that it was so, it was as though the sun had suddenly gone out. They had no hope left.

Some of the men said: "It is certain that God has cast us off and will no longer be our God. What is there for us to do but to worship the gods of Babylon and pray that they will give us better success?"

That night Ezekiel told the elders of a vision he had had of a valley filled with dry bones. He heard a voice saying, "Son of man, can these bones live?" Of course, he knew that would be impossible, and yet, as he watched, it seemed as though the bones became men and stood up alive. Then he heard the voice telling him what the vision meant. "Son of man, these bones are the whole people of Israel. There seems to be no hope for them. But when the Spirit of God breathes upon them they will come to life again and stand upon their feet and begin to be a great people once more."

From that day Ezekiel taught the exiles that God still had a plan for them and they need not despair. They could serve him as his people even though Jerusalem was destroyed and they were living in a foreign land.

When the exiles first came to Tel-abib, they had no time or place for worship. Many were sure that it was not possible to worship God in a strange land. "It is in Jerusalem alone that the God of Israel is known, not in Babylon or other lands," they said. So they would think sadly of how once they went up to sing and pray and offer their sacrifices in the Temple.

One of them wrote a song about this and soon all of them knew it:

"As the deer pants for brooks of water,
So longs my soul for thee, O God.
My soul thirsts for God, for the living God.
When shall I come and appear before God?
I went with all the people,
I went with them to the house of God
With the voice of joy and praise,
With all that kept holyday."

There were other verses, but before it ended, the song said something that kept those that sang it from being discouraged:

"Why are you cast down, my soul?
Why are you so troubled?
Hope still in God, for I shall yet praise him.
He is the health of my life and my God."

Simeon and Abigail remembered the songs of the Temple in Jerusalem, and sometimes they sang them when they had finished the evening meal. The boys learned them quickly. As they sang, it seemed to them that God was not far away at all.

"I will lift up my eyes to the hills
From whence cometh my help.
My help cometh from the Lord
Who made heaven and earth."

Often two or three families would gather in one house to sing the songs of their people. One of the older men would tell stories of the things that had happened long ago—of Abraham and Moses and David and Elijah.

Then the elders and the priests decided that each Sabbath Day all the people would go out by the side of the canal to worship together. There they sang the old songs and recited prayers. There too the priests taught the people the laws they must keep if they would be loyal to their God.

Sometimes word came to Tel-abib of other colonies of Jews, as the people from Judah were now called. Many of them were in Babylonia, but there were some in nearly every land. Young men from Tel-abib became soldiers in the Babylonian army. As they traveled through different lands, they were always meeting people from Samaria or Jerusalem. In Egypt, the Jews were free to go where they liked. Some were businessmen, some were farmers, and some were soldiers. Most of them did not want ever to go back to Palestine again.

In Palestine there were still many people, but most of their cities and towns had been destroyed and they were very poor. Often they lived in caves, where they were safest from the robbers who roamed the land.

It did not seem possible to these scattered Jews that they would ever be a nation again. Their sons and daughters were marrying the foreign people among whom they lived. Children were growing up to live like the foreigners and worship the foreign gods.

But there were some who believed that God still had a purpose for his people. They might be scattered now through all the lands, but one day God would gather them together again in their own land. They believed what the prophets had taught them—that God had scattered them and made them suffer so that they might learn to be truly his people.

These men began to write the story of all the things that had happened to Israel in the past, so that the people might see how God had led them. The priests had brought from Palestine books of history and of law and books in which the messages of the prophets were written. Sometimes there were two books telling the same story, one that had been written in Israel and the other in Judah. Now they put them together and made one story that seemed always to be saying one thing: "God promised to be our God if we would be his people, but we rejected him and brought trouble upon ourselves."

So the long years passed. The older exiles died but many more were born. And to the children the story was told over and over how once the people of Israel had been free in their own land.

There was excitement among all the older people one day when it was known that Nethaniah had received a long letter from Palestine. It was not often that any letter came. The elders were not surprised that Nethaniah called them to his home that night.

"A great new prophet has arisen," Nethaniah began, "and to us and to the other colonies have come written copies of his message. I have never seen anything to compare with his words. Listen while I read:

" 'Comfort you, comfort you my people, saith your
    God;
  Speak encouragingly to Jerusalem.
  Cry unto her that her time of hard service is
    finished. Her wrongdoing is pardoned.'

"He says that God is coming to gather us like a shepherd gathers his sheep and to make a new day for us. I know that some of you think God will have nothing more to do with us, but hear what the prophet says:

" 'Why do you say, O Jacob, and you, O Israel,
That your way is hid from God and that God has
    not been just to you?
Have you not known? Have you not heard?
The everlasting God, the Lord, the Creator of
    the ends of the earth,
Does not faint or grow weary.
There is no searching of his understanding.
He gives power to the faint and the weak he
    makes strong.
Even young men shall grow faint and weary,
But those who trust in God shall get new
    strength;
They shall mount up with wings like eagles;
They shall run and not grow weary.
They shall walk and not be tired.' "

On the Sabbath, Nethaniah read the messages to all the people. He could not tell the people who the prophet was, but that did not matter. It was as though God himself was speaking to them and breathing new hope and strength into their hearts.

Other letters came and were read to the people at

the Sabbath meetings. Sometimes the prophet wrote of how foolish it was for anyone to carve idols out of wood and then bow down and worship them instead of worshiping the living God who made heaven and earth. Often he wrote of how Israel was still God's special servant and his chosen people. Even though they had often rejected him, God had made known among them a truth that could change the lives of all men. The prophet was always pleading for his people to see the great work there was for them to do. If only they would trust God, they would find that he was keeping the promises he had made long before to Abraham and to Moses.

But in Tel-abib it was hard not to be discouraged.
Simeon and Nethaniah and the others who had come
there as young men were now old and could never
make a long journey. They knew that whatever happened they would die in Babylonia. Many of the
younger people were anxious to forget what had happened in the past and to become as much like the
Babylonians as possible. But even among the younger
ones there were always some who said, "Perhaps God
has some great purpose for us yet."

9. Rebuilding

THE BOYS hurried down the path to the house of the young priest Nathan. Nathan did not like it if they were late. The last time, he had made them memorize a proverb about learning from the ants how to be wise. They had to say it aloud, and when they came to the words, "How long will you sleep, O lazy one?", all the other boys laughed at them.

Nathan often taught them proverbs. The first words he spoke to them when they started in his school had been a proverb: "The fear of the Lord is the beginning of knowledge: but fools despise wisdom and instruction." The fear of the Lord—that meant honoring the God of their fathers and loving him with all their heart and soul.

The boys were nearly breathless when they reached the house—and they were late! But strangely Nathan did not seem to notice. He was excited about something, and his eyes were shining.

"It is fifty-eight years since our fathers first came as prisoners to this land," he began, "but now, God be thanked, perhaps we shall return to our own country. Cyrus, king of Persia, is approaching the gates of Babylon, and soon our oppressors will be overthrown. No nation can hold out against him."

Instead of going on with the lessons of the day, Nathan brought out a box that the boys had seen before. In it were sheets of parchment on which he had been copying sayings from the ancient books. They told of a great new day that was coming.

"Jeremiah said that it would be seventy years before we would return to Jerusalem," said Nathan, holding one of the sheets in his hand. "God will make a new covenant with us and write his law in our hearts. Then all of us will know what is right without being taught."

"If Jeremiah is right, we'll have to wait more than ten years, won't we?" said one of the boys.

"Perhaps God will have mercy on us and not make us wait so long," answered Nathan, picking up more of the writings. "Here are the words of two prophets who live today. The first says, 'God is sending the Medes against Babylon to destroy all its power and beauty and to set the house of Israel free once more.' The other tells us that God himself is coming to save

138

us and to gather us from all the lands. Listen:

" 'Then the eyes of the blind shall be opened
And the ears of the deaf shall be unstopped.
Then shall the lame man leap like a deer,
And the man who was dumb shall sing.
And the ransomed of the Lord shall return
And come with singing unto Zion.
Everlasting joy shall be upon their heads;
They shall have gladness and joy,
And sorrow and sighing shall flee away.'

"Some say that it is God himself who will appear to
be our King. Others think that he will send King David back to rule for him. However that may be, it will
be a glorious day."

The boys listened, not understanding everything
Nathan read, but feeling how wonderful it was that
God was going to do these things for their people.

Soon Cyrus was in Babylon. The people of the city
hated their king, Nabonidus, so they opened their
gates to Cyrus and welcomed him. There was little
fighting and Babylon was not destroyed at all.

Among the Jews there was great excitement when
word came that Cyrus would let all go free who wished
to return to Palestine. Nathan and many others were
sure that the day the prophets had promised was
about to dawn. They could hardly wait to begin the
journey. They wanted everyone to go with them.

Jonathan the goldsmith did not agree with Nathan. "Why should I leave Tel-abib?" he asked the priest. "I am not young any more, and the journey would be too hard for me. Besides, I do not imagine there would be much for a goldsmith to do in Jerusalem. From what I hear it is a poor, barren country. Go if you must, but do not expect me to go with you."

There were many who thought as Jonathan did. They did not intend to leave their homes and businesses and friends in Babylonia to go back and start life over in Palestine. They would help those who went and send money with them, but they themselves would not go.

The caravan, when it was ready, was very different from the one that had come across the desert nearly sixty years before. Then the people had walked on foot. Now they rode on camels and donkeys. Then they were prisoners, hungry, weary, and helpless. Now they were free men, with plenty of supplies for their journey, with gold in their money pouches, and with joy in their hearts.

Nathan was disappointed when he reached Jerusalem. He had read about the city and sung about it so often that he had expected it to be more wonderful than any other city, even though it was in ruins. But everywhere he looked he could see only stones and more stones, lying in heaps and scattered over the hills. Here and there were little houses among the ruins.

There was work for all of them to do. First they

cleared a space in the Temple courts and made an altar, so that Jeshua the high priest could offer the daily sacrifice. Then they had to build houses, for they were still living in the tents they had used in traveling. Since Zerubbabel had been appointed as their governor, there had to be a large house for him. Most of the people built houses just big enough for the family to sleep inside. Next, Zerubbabel set everyone to work on the walls of the Temple. Jeshua and the other priests had to show the governor and his men the plan from which the Temple was to be built.

Then came a bitter disappointment.

As if the difficulties they had already were not enough, the Jews discovered that there were people in the land who were their enemies. Many Jews who had not been carried away to Babylon when Jerusalem was destroyed were still living in Judah and Samaria and among them were also foreigners who had come on from other lands. Some, particularly in Judah, were glad to see the exiles return from Babylon and joined with them in rebuilding the city. But there were others who were not pleased. They had mingled so freely with the unbelievers that they no longer felt close to their own people; the worship of the God of their fathers meant little to them. They feared now that the Jews who had returned would try to lord it over them.

Soon these people sent a letter to King Cyrus, warning him that if he let Jerusalem be built there

would be trouble. Word came back that the work on the walls and the Temple must stop! The people of Jerusalem were fearful and easily discouraged. They obeyed the king's command.

Years went by. The people tore down their little houses and made better ones. Jerusalem began to look more like a city again. But in the Temple courts there was only the altar, for the Temple was not yet built.

There was one prophet in Jerusalem who told the people that the Temple was not the most important thing.

"God does not live in a house of stone and wood," he said. "The whole of heaven and earth is his house. Wherever people are humble and obey God's word, he dwells with them."

This prophet was angry when the people thought they could please God merely by going without food on the fast days.

"This is not what God asks us to do," he told them. "God wants us to share our bread with the hungry and see that the poor have clothing to cover them. If anyone is made a slave, we must set him free. If we do these things, then truly God will be with us and he will help us build a new city and a new nation."

Many of the people listened to the prophet. It seemed that God was speaking to them through him, just as he had spoken long ago through Elijah and Amos and Isaiah. As they listened, they did not care how poor they were or how hard it was to live in Jerusalem. Their hearts were filled with hope and joy when they heard him say: "You are the people of God. Through all the years he has been making you ready to carry his truth to all nations."

Jeshua, the high priest, was not pleased at what the prophet said. In fact he did not like him at all. What would happen to the nation and its religion if this fellow was permitted to speak against the fast days and the sacrifices and the Temple?

Jeshua was better pleased when two prophets named Haggai and Zechariah began urging the people

to rebuild the Temple. All that year there had been little rain. The crops in the fields were burned up by the sun before they could ripen. There were many hungry people in Judea.

"You wonder why things do not go well for you," said Haggai. "It is because you have fine houses for yourselves, but the Lord's house is still in ruins. Go up to the forest of Lebanon and bring wood and build the Temple again."

This time no one was able to stop the building. The king of Persia had given orders that no one was to interfere. Slowly the walls rose as the great stones were set one upon the other, and workmen brought huge timbers from the forest to hold up the roof. Zerubbabel set every man who could be spared from other work to help in the building.

144

Some of the older men said, "It is not like the wonderful Temple that Solomon built."

Some of the young men who had come from Babylonia and Egypt said, "It is not nearly so fine as the temples of other gods that we have seen."

When Zechariah heard what they were saying he answered them. "God's word to you is this: 'It is not by might, or by power, but by my spirit that great things are done. Why do you despise the day of small things?' From these small beginnings God can bring a great new day for his people."

So the Temple was built, but the walls of the city were still in ruins, and the people who lived there had no protection against their enemies. Sometimes they wondered if they should have stayed in Babylonia and not come back to Jerusalem at all.

There were far more Jews in other lands than there were in Judea. In Babylonia some of them grew very wealthy, as the years passed, and even became advisers to the king. In Egypt they lived in many towns, and in one place they had a temple of their own. But, wherever they were, they could not forget that their God was different from the gods of the people among whom they lived, and that he expected their ways to be different from the ways of other people.

Sometimes their neighbors would say: "Why do these Jews not worship our gods or do the things we do? Do they think they are better than we are?"

But there were times when the very opposite happened and their neighbors said: "The God whom these Jews worship is a God of truth and justice and not like our cruel gods. We too will worship him."

So in many lands there were more and more people coming to know the true God. It had seemed at first to be a great misfortune that the Jews were carried from their homes in Palestine and scattered to the north, south, east, and west. But now God was using them wherever they were to help others to know him.

It was more than seventy years before the walls of Jerusalem were built. Because there were no walls, no one in Jerusalem could ever feel safe, for enemies could come in upon them whenever they wished. The people longed for the day when they could lock their gates and set guards upon the gate towers to protect the city. Then perhaps Jerusalem would be a happier place in which to live.

At last Jerusalem found the friend it needed.

The capital city of the Persian Empire was at Susa in the mountains east of Babylon, and the cupbearer of King Artaxerxes in Susa was a Jew named Nehemiah. He was much respected by the king and had great power. Certain men from Judea came to him one day, and he questioned them about what was happening in Jerusalem and Judah. When he learned that the city still had no walls or gates, and that the people were very poor and unhappy, he could not rest

until he had found some way of helping them.

First Nehemiah went to his own room and prayed. He thought of the great troubles that had come upon his people because they refused to do God's will. He remembered the promise God had made that, if they would return to him with all their heart, he would gather them from all countries and bring them to their own home again. He knew that God would keep his promise. So Nehemiah prayed that God would show him some good plan to bring help to the people of Judah.

It was not many days until Nehemiah had permission from Artaxerxes to go to Judah. He was to cut timbers in the king's forests for the new gates and to gather stones for the walls. But when Nehemiah arrived in Palestine, he told no one what he was going to do, not even the chief men in the city. He knew that the enemies of Jerusalem would try to keep him from building up the walls.

The fourth night he was there he got up when everyone was asleep. With just a few of his men he went out to inspect the walls and to plan the work. Often the horse he was riding could find no path because of the rocks and rubbish that were scattered everywhere.

In the morning Nehemiah called together the rulers of the city, with the priests and nobles, and laid his plan before them. He told them that God had put it in his heart to do this thing for Jerusalem and that he had the permission of the king to carry it through.

At once the whole city set to work, each man with his family and his servants having one part of the wall to build. Many chieftains from outside Jerusalem in Judah came with their families and each agreed to take a share in the building. Even the children and the women helped, carrying stones for the workmen.

At first the enemies of Jerusalem mocked at what the people were doing. "The wall those weaklings put up will not be strong enough to keep out even a fox," they said. But when they saw a strong wall rising on every side of Jerusalem, they became frightened and angry. Their leaders met together and agreed to attack Jerusalem before the walls became too strong.

Nehemiah learned of the danger from Jews who lived in other parts of the country and who had heard of the plan from their neighbors. Then Nehemiah gave a new order.

"Let men from every family be appointed to stand ready with swords and spears and bows, so that no sudden attack may surprise us. Let also the workmen keep their weapons near by, and be ready to seize them at a moment's notice."

When the enemies saw that the people of Jerusalem were on guard, they let them alone. Steadily the wall rose, until it was finished, and the gates were set on their hinges to keep Jerusalem safe by day and by night.

Nehemiah soon learned that more was needed in the city than new walls. Poor people came to him and complained that they were without food because rich men had taken their farms. Sometimes they were even sold into slavery because of their debts.

Nehemiah called the rulers together again. He made them promise that such things would not be done any longer, and that every Jew who had been made a slave should go free. He asked them, "How can you expect God to have mercy upon you if you have no mercy or kindness toward each other?"

Nehemiah soon saw that the people were constantly doing wrong because they were ignorant of God's law. The priests and the scribes had books of the law and writings of the prophets. But many of the people had never read them, nor heard them read. For them it was as though Moses and Elijah and Amos and Jeremiah had never lived.

Not long before, there had come from Babylon a scribe named Ezra, who knew far better than most men the laws of God. The command was sent to all the people to gather in the square beside the fish gate. When all were there, Ezra stood on a platform before them and read to them from the Book of the Law. No longer could any of them say that they had not heard it. Then Nehemiah told the people that from that day only those who were willing to keep God's law would be allowed to live in Jerusalem.

There were some in Jerusalem who were sure that if only every Jew would obey God's law, the great new day of peace and plenty for which they hoped would come at once. There were others who were sure that men would never obey God's law rightly until God should send them a leader and saviour who would be greater than Moses or Elijah.

10. Losing the Way

FOR HUNDREDS of years in Israel and Judah men had gone to the prophets when they wanted to know God's will for them. They knew that the prophets were spokesmen for God. But after the time of Nehemiah and Ezra, they went instead to the scribes, who knew more about the books of the Law than anyone else. They no longer needed prophets, they said, since the sacred books would tell them what God wanted them to do. So for hundreds of years there were no prophets among the Jews.

One thing they found written in the Law was that Jews should not marry with people of other nations round about. This law had been made because so many Jews married foreigners and then became like the foreigners in their ways instead of being true to their own God and his ways. The leaders were afraid that, unless something was done about this, Israel would simply disappear.

There were many in Jerusalem who were very angry when all foreign wives and husbands were told that they must leave the city. Some of them took their families to Samaria, where, joining with the people who lived there, they built another temple. They said that it was more truly the temple of God than the one in Jerusalem. From that time on there was even greater hatred than before between the people of Samaria and the people of Judah.

The people in Jerusalem read in the books of the prophets that a wonderful time of peace and plenty would someday come for their city and they would be made rulers over the whole earth. They thought that God should not let the other nations have any part in it. These nations had been so cruel to the Jews that the Jews now hoped God would destroy them completely. Hardly anyone remembered that God's promise to Abraham was not just for the Jewish nation, but that through him and his people all nations would be blessed. There was no longer any prophet to tell them that all people belonged to God and that he wanted all of them to be gathered into his family.

Not everyone thought it was right to hate foreigners. One man wrote a little book to show how foolish it was. He told the story of a prophet named Jonah, whom God sent to preach to the foreigners in Nineveh. Jonah, like so many of the Jews, did not want the people of Nineveh to repent of their sins; instead he hoped that God would destroy them. So he went aboard a ship to sail as far away from Nineveh as he could. When a terrible storm threatened to wreck the ship, Jonah saw in it God's anger at his disobedience and had the sailors throw him into the sea. He was swallowed by a great fish and was cast up by the fish on the land again, where once more he heard God commanding him to go to Nineveh. This time he went; and when he preached, the people repented of their sins. Then Jonah did something that was very strange and foolish for a prophet to do: he became very angry because, now that the people of Nineveh had repented, God would have mercy on them and forgive them.

When people read this book, they knew that the writer was making fun of the way they hated foreigners. He was trying to make them see that God wanted all men in all the world to turn from evil ways and truly live as his people.

After the Persians had ruled Palestine for a long time, the Greeks, under Alexander the Great, came marching into the land and conquered it.

The Greeks were great lovers of games and music

and all things that would give them pleasure. The streets were lined with rows of tall, graceful columns. They built new cities in Palestine, and the buildings were more beautiful than any the Jews had ever seen. In every city they had theaters, where they went to see plays, and places for all kinds of sports and games. Many Greeks came to live in Palestine and taught the people of Palestine to worship the Greek gods.

Soon young Jews began to like the Greek ways better than their own. It was fun to play the games of their Greek friends and listen to their music and read their books. But few were content to do only that. They began also to go to the Greek temples to worship Greek gods. They wanted no one to speak to them any longer about the God of Israel and his law. They were ashamed to dress or to talk or to act as their own people did, for they wished to be like their Greek friends in everything.

As the years passed, there were more and more young men who wanted to put aside the teachings of the Prophets and of the old Jewish law and to copy foreign ways. At last they were more powerful than the faithful Jews in Jerusalem. They had one of their men appointed high priest and set up the images of the Greek gods, even in the Temple itself. The Syrians who were now trying to rule Palestine helped them. It was like the days of Ahab and Elijah, when the prophets of Baal drove out the worshipers of the true God.

Those who were faithful to God had to flee for their lives and live in caves in the hills for safety. Then God raised up new leaders for them—an old priest, Mattathias, and his five sons, who were named the Maccabees. They called together all who were faithful and trained an army. Again and again they defeated the armies of the Syrians. Because they were fighting to defend their faith it seemed as though no one could stand against them.

So successful were the sons of Mattathias that Judea (as Judah was now called) became a kingdom again, more powerful than any of its neighbors. It was stronger and richer than it had ever been since the time of David.

During the struggle between the Jews and the Syrians, the Jews often had to endure great suffering for their faith. To encourage them a book was written which all of them read eagerly. It told the story of Daniel and his brave companions who, long years before, held fast to the faith of their fathers in spite of everything men did to them. Daniel was tempted to copy the ways of the Babylonians and to worship their images, but he refused to do anything that was against the law of the God of Israel. The Jews who followed the Maccabees read these stories over and over, and it helped them to be faithful in their day, even though their enemies burned their homes and tortured them.

XZW‡‡११

In many parts of the world people had begun to speak and write in the Greek language. In Egypt many of the Jews had stopped using the Hebrew language. Nearly everything was now written or spoken in Greek. The Jewish children growing up in Egypt no longer knew how to read or speak Hebrew and, therefore, could no longer read the books of the Law and the Prophets.

The elders knew that if their people could not understand the sacred books they would forget all about their religion. So they started with the book of Genesis and wrote it in the Greek language for the people to read. Then they did the same with Exodus, and with each of the sacred books. It took them many years to do it, but when they had finished, anyone who could read Greek could learn what God had been saying to Israel through all the years. Before this, no one could read these books unless he knew the Hebrew language.

ΕΝ ΑΡΧΗ

Some of the elders did not want this Greek translation of the Scriptures to be made. They said that they were not the true Scriptures unless they were in Hebrew, as they were first written. But the others believed that it was more important to have them written so that all the people could read and understand.

In Palestine the new kingdom did not last very long. The people could not agree with each other. Some leaders, who were called Sadducees, were rich and powerful and proud, but they were not very careful in keeping the law of God. There were others called Pharisees who were often very poor and were always studying the law to know what God wanted them to do. They kept the laws very strictly and they added many new laws that were not written in the ancient books. They were sure that God would be more pleased with them than with the Sadducees.

The Sadducees and the Pharisees quarreled so much that the kingdom became weak. Finally they could not agree who should be their ruler, so they asked a Roman general to settle the dispute for them. He settled it by coming with his army and taking control of the land.

Under the Romans the Jews were unhappier than they had ever been before. The Roman soldiers kept order in the land, but they were cruel and heartless. They made the people pay heavy taxes, so that the farmers and the fishermen could hardly buy enough food to feed their children. Everyone hated the Romans, but even more they hated those of their own people who made a good profit for themselves by working as publicans, or taxgatherers, for the Romans.

It was an unhappy time for poor people in Palestine—and most of the people were poor. The Pharisees told them that God would punish them if they did not keep every law, both little and great, but there were so many laws that hardly anyone knew what they all were. There was not much chance of pleasing God unless a man did nothing but study the law. It made the people afraid of God.

They had to be afraid of the Romans too. If they failed to pay their taxes, they might be sold as slaves. Sometimes Jews tried to rebel as the Maccabees had done, but the Romans took the rebel leaders out and nailed them up on crosses as a warning to the rest.

There were other things the poor people feared, such as sickness. When a man was sick, there was no one to take care of his family. There were many sicknesses that no one knew how to cure. They were also afraid of evil spirits which, they thought, lived all around them and were waiting to do them harm.

In every town there was a synagogue where the Jews went each Sabbath to worship. There the people heard readings from the Law and the Prophets which told them of a time when there would no longer be any sorrow or unhappiness. It would be a day of joy and peace and freedom and plenty for all. They prayed and prayed that the day would come and that

163

everything would be changed for them. But it seemed as though it would never come. When they went out into the streets again, the Romans were still there. Everyone was as full of fear and hatred as before.

There was great excitement among the Jews all over Palestine when it was reported that a prophet was preaching near the Jordan. There had been no prophet in Israel for a long, long time.

"What is he saying?" they asked. Those who had been to hear him said that it was as though Elijah or Jeremiah had come back from the dead. The prophet's name was John, and he was calling upon everyone, even the Pharisees and priests, to repent of their sins and return to God.

"You should have seen how angry the Pharisees were," said one man. "They told John that they were children of Abraham, and God's people by birth, and that it was an insult to them to say that they should repent and change their ways."

"What did John answer them?" asked one of the listeners.

"He made them angrier than ever," the man went on. "He said that God could make children of Abraham out of the very stones if he wanted to do it, but that God would have nothing to do with them unless they had a more humble spirit."

The poor people who had so much to endure went to hear John more than any others. John told them that the day of joy and peace and freedom for which they longed was coming soon. But he said that every man who wanted to share in it must be willing to turn back to God and trust him with all his heart and mind and soul. Those who were willing to begin a new life he baptized, as a sign that God was making their whole life clean. Because he did this, men called him John the Baptizer. As the people went back to their homes they had already a strength and joy that they had not known before.

Herod was now the ruler in Judea, governing it for the Romans. He hated John because the prophet had accused him before everyone of having done wrong. The priests were afraid of John because he was so popular with the people. The Pharisees did not like him because he treated them as though they were no more important to God than anyone else. But there were many everywhere in Palestine to whom John brought hope of a new day. When they heard him speak, they knew that things could be different if only men would let God be their King.

11. He Who Comes

MANY people came from Galilee to the Jordan to hear the prophet John—fishermen, farmers, workmen, and even the "teachers of religion." Some of them were so sure he was right that they stayed with him part of the time to help him with his work.

John told them that soon God would send them a leader, the Messiah, who would be far greater than he. When people asked John how to get ready for the coming of the Messiah, he answered: "Change your hearts and your ways. Do as God wants you to do. Share your food and clothing with those who have none. Be just and honest with everyone."

The people of Judea who went out to hear John did not like to see so many Galileans. They prided themselves upon having lived in Judea for hundreds of years, and despised the Jews who lived in the north, in Galilee, because there were so many foreigners in that part of the country. The prophet, however, did not care where a man came from if he was in earnest about repenting and doing the will of God. He said that God would be able to do greater things in Judea if the Judeans were not so proud of themselves.

One day John baptized a new follower from Galilee. No one had ever seen him before. John and he talked together for hours. John's disciples wondered who this man was.

"His name is Jesus. He told one of the men that he is from Nazareth," said Andrew, a fisherman from Bethsaida on the Sea of Galilee. Andrew had been a disciple of the prophet for some time.

"I heard him talking with the prophet this morning," said a friend of Andrew. "It sounded as though he knows more than the prophet does. I wish we could talk with him."

The next day Andrew's friend had his wish, for he and Andrew were invited by Jesus to spend the evening with him. When they came away, they were excited as they had never been before.

"John is a great prophet," said Andrew, "but Jesus is greater. When we talked with him, I felt as though I had never known the truth before."

"What shall we do?" his friend asked him. "If we become followers of Jesus, we must leave the prophet, for soon Jesus will be going north into Galilee to preach. He does not intend to stay here with John very long. I do not want to leave John, and yet I feel I must go with Jesus."

The two men went to their master, the prophet, and told him what they were thinking. They were surprised when he smiled and said that he had expected they would leave him to become followers of Jesus. He seemed sure that Jesus was going to do a greater work than he ever could and that he would need brave followers.

Jesus told Andrew and the others that he was not yet ready to begin his work. When he was ready, he would let them know. When that time came, they would have to give up their fishing and go with him wherever he went.

While Jesus was with the prophet John, he was making plans. When he was baptized by John, he had heard God saying to him, "Thou art my beloved Son, in whom I am well pleased." To be God's beloved Son meant to be the Messiah for whom the Jews had been hoping for hundreds of years. But if Jesus said openly that he was the Messiah, everyone would expect him suddenly to show great power and to become a great king, with armies to do his bidding. Jesus knew that God's Messiah was not that kind of king. In the Scriptures it was written that he would be gentle and peaceful, and that his word of truth would be stronger than all the powers of the world. Jesus knew also that it was written in the Scriptures that God's servants always had to suffer for truth and right.

Because he did not want anyone to misunderstand, Jesus did not tell even his closest friends that he was the Messiah. That would be his secret until they understood what he intended to do. When that day came, they would know for themselves who he was, without having to be told.

Jesus went away into the hill country near the Jordan to be alone and to think about all that he must do. For many days he did not even eat. While he was there, he was tempted to turn aside from what God wanted him to do. Far more people would follow him if he would offer them an easy way to get food, or if he would astonish them with a miracle, or set himself up as king and compel them to do his bidding. But Jesus knew that none of these was the way in which God planned to save his people. God's way was slower and quieter and more difficult.

When these temptations were past, Jesus was ready to begin his work. He was ready for whatever might happen.

The prophet John usually preached at a place in the rough country beside the Jordan River. The people had to leave their homes in the hills and valleys of Palestine and go down to the Jordan if they wanted to hear him. When Jesus began to preach, he did not do as John had done. He traveled through the towns and villages, preaching to the people where they were.

John said, "God is waiting for you to turn back to him." So John waited for the people to come.

Jesus said: "God is like a shepherd, and you are like sheep that he has lost. In love he will search for you until he finds you." So Jesus went out along the roads of Palestine, and into the houses and through the streets of the towns, searching for people who had forgotten God.

Wherever Jesus went, he told people that God was not far away, but near. God would make their whole life different if they would trust him completely and do his will.

When Jesus met a poor man, he told him that God could give him joy and strength and peace, which would be better than money. But when he met rich men, he warned them that if they were selfish, they would shut themselves out from God.

People came to him who were sorrowful, and they went away joyful. But those who could think of nothing except how to enjoy themselves became unhappy when they were in Jesus' company.

There were many who were discouraged and did not think that it mattered much whether they lived or died. But when they had listened to Jesus, they knew that God had a plan for every day and hour of their lives, and that God was always thinking of them as the children of his great family. There were others who were sure that they were God's people and who always acted as though they were better than anyone else. But Jesus told them that they should trust humbly in God and not in their own goodness.

Many people loved Jesus dearly because of what he had done for them, and they were ready to do anything for him. But the ones whom Jesus warned not to be so selfish and satisfied with themselves called him a troublemaker and were sorry when he came to their town.

One thing that astonished everyone was the way Jesus seemed to be able to make sick people well. As soon as he came into a town, men and women and children with all kinds of sicknesses hurried to the place where he was. Sometimes they had to be carried there by their friends.

Jesus knew that some sicknesses were caused by things that people had done wrong. What they did made them unhappy in their own minds, and this unhappiness made them sick in their bodies. That was why often when Jesus healed a man he said to him, "Your sins are forgiven." When their sins were forgiven, their bodies became whole and strong again.

There were religious leaders who were always watching what Jesus did. They said: "Does he think that he is God? Only God can forgive sins." They were sure that Jesus was teaching the people falsely.

Soon it was time for Jesus to carry out the next step in his plan. He needed men who would learn to teach and heal as he did. By himself he could visit only a few towns and villages and could teach only a few people. But if he had disciples, many more people would be able to hear the good news that he had for them.

Jesus knew where to find Andrew and some others that he had met when he was with John the Baptizer. There was Andrew's brother Simon, and their friends John and James. All four of them were fishermen at Capernaum on the northern shore of the Sea of Galilee. One day when they were sitting in their boats near the shore mending their nets, Jesus came and told them that he needed them now to help him.

Many people were surprised at the kind of men Jesus chose to be his disciples. One of them, Matthew,

had been a taxgatherer, and everybody knew that
taxgatherers cheated people and were heartless in
their demands for money. The people in Capernaum thought that Jesus' fishermen friends were not
as good or as religious as some other people in the city.
They did not understand what Jesus wanted when he
chose a disciple. It did not matter to him how good or
bad the man had been, but only whether he was willing from that time on to let God rule his life completely.

One young man who came to talk with Jesus had a great disappointment. He asked Jesus what he must do to be sure that he would have eternal life. He said that he had kept God's laws from the time he was a child, but he felt that perhaps God expected something more of him.

The man was very rich, with a fine house and many servants. But Jesus knew that none of these things could ever make him happy. As Jesus talked with him, he asked him to give up all his riches and become a disciple, traveling with him from town to town.

When the young man heard what Jesus wanted him to do, he was even more unhappy than he had been before. He still wanted to be a follower of Jesus, but he could not bear to give up all the good things that his money bought for him. And Jesus would not let him be a disciple as long as he loved his possessions more than he loved God.

At last there were twelve disciples who were with Jesus everywhere he went. What little money they had was kept by Judas, who had been appointed treasurer. If people gave them gifts to help them in their work, the money was given to Judas and he used it to buy food or anything else they needed. When they were staying a few days in a town, the people usually took them into their homes for the night and gave them their meals. There were times, however, when they slept under the stars because they had not been invited to anyone's home.

The disciples wanted to understand Jesus better, so they listened carefully when he was teaching the crowds. But when they were alone with him, they always had many questions for him to answer. He talked with them while they were walking from town to town or after the people had all gone away at night or before the crowds began to come in the morning.

At the time they became disciples Jesus warned each one of them how hard it was going to be, and they soon found out what he meant. He would not let them stop working as long as there was anyone to be helped. He would not let them keep even food or clothing for themselves if someone needed it more than they did. But, hardest of all, they had to speak the truth to the people even though they were hated for doing it. When people treated them cruelly, Jesus did not let them strike back. He said that to return evil for evil only made two evils; they must return good for evil and love for hate. Only in this way would evil and hatred be overcome in men's hearts. The disciples often talked among themselves about how hard it was to do this.

Sometimes when the disciples awoke in the morning, Jesus was nowhere to be seen. After a time he would come down the hill outside the town and have his breakfast with them. They knew that long before sunrise, while they were still sleeping, Jesus had been high up on the hills, where he could look out over the whole countryside, praying and planning what he must do. Each time he came back he was stronger and more able to meet every difficulty. They wished that they could pray as he did. When they told Jesus what they wished, at once he taught them a prayer that would show them what all their prayers should be like.

There were times when Jesus took the disciples with him to a quiet place in the hills, where they could be undisturbed by the crowds for a few days. There was so much he had to teach them and so little time!

It was not easy for James and Simon and John and the others to understand Jesus' plan for them.

"You are the light of the world," he told them. Then he would show them in the Scriptures how God had been trying to send the light of his truth to all nations. He had chosen Israel to be his people, that the light might shine in them and go out from them to the world. He had sent his prophets to remind them what his purpose was. But time after time they had refused to obey him. Even now, though the priests and the Pharisees and many of the Jews were very sure that they were God's own people, they were interested only in saving themselves and not in the saving of the whole world.

Then the disciples began to understand why Jesus had chosen them. Because the whole nation would not do what God wanted them to do, God was making a new beginning with these few men. They would be his people and would serve him. They would be the first; then others would join them. Through them the whole world would come to know God and his truth. All men would learn to live together as his family. That was what Jesus meant when he looked at them with joy in his eyes and said: "You are the salt of the earth! You are the light of the world!"

He warned them that if they were unfaithful to God's light and truth, God would cast them aside just as, many times before, he had cast aside those who had forgotten him. But if they were faithful, they would not have to fear anyone. Men would try to stop them in what they were doing and might even kill them. But, no matter what happened, God would be with them. He would make the light shine out farther and farther until it reached across the whole earth.

12. Time to Decide

Love your enemies, and pray for those who injure you. If you love only those who love you and are good to you, there is nothing remarkable about that. But if you return love for hatred and good for evil, then all men will know that you are my disciples."

The disciples were sitting listening while Jesus talked. Down below the hill they could see the waters of the Sea of Galilee, with the sails of fishing boats moving here and there. In the towns on the shore were the people whom it was so hard to love: Roman soldiers, with their swords and spears; taxgatherers, with their clanking bags of money; Pharisees, who were always accusing the disciples of teaching the people falsely; thieves; drunkards; and a host of others.

"Master, it is all very well to say, 'Love your enemies' while we are up here, but when we go back into the town and have to meet them every day and live with them it is a different matter. I don't see how we can do it." It was John who spoke, but some of the others nodded their heads to show that they agreed with him.

"I told you when you became my disciples that you would have to do what no one else has ever dreamed of doing," Jesus answered them. "I told you that it would cost you your pride and perhaps more suffering than you would want to bear. Unless your love is like God's, forgiving men their evil again and again until the evil is overcome, you are not true followers of mine."

Jesus said no more. Nor did any of the others say anything. Suddenly it had flashed into their minds that Jesus himself had shown all along that it was possible to love even one's enemies. He was doing it. He never tried to get back at anyone who injured him. He was firm with them, but understanding and forgiving. When a disciple made a mistake, Jesus told him about it quickly, but all the time the disciple knew that Jesus was not against him, but rather was giving him a chance to do better.

The most religious people did not understand Jesus very well. He did not do what they expected him to do. They thought that a good man should stay among good people. But Jesus made friends with men and women who, everyone said, were bad. Then, too, the religious people thought that a prophet should be very sad and stern. They were surprised when they saw Jesus laughing and talking while he had supper with his friends.

Matthew, the disciple who had been a taxgatherer, took Jesus to meet other taxgatherers. Most people hated these men and would have nothing to do with them, but Jesus went to their homes and talked with them. No one had ever tried to help them before. Sometimes they wrote to their fellow taxgatherers in other towns, telling them to be sure to see Jesus if he came to their town. One of these was Zacchaeus in Jericho, in whose home Jesus visited. Many people in the town were angry at Jesus for going there. They did not know until later that something had happened to Zacchaeus when Jesus went to stay with him. He decided to give away half of all his money to care for poor people, and he promised that whatever he had taken wrongly from any man he would repay four times over. He was happier than he had ever been before when Jesus said to him, "Zacchaeus, today salvation has come to your house."

Whenever anyone criticized Jesus for spending his time with people such as Zacchaeus, Jesus answered them that he was like a doctor and that it would be foolish for a doctor to be always among those who were well, and not with the sick who needed him. His answer did not make the good religious people love him any better.

Another thing that made religious people angry with Jesus was that he did not keep all the rules that they kept. They were sure that it was wrong to do work of any kind on the Sabbath Day. But Jesus said that God's law of mercy and love was greater than the Sabbath law, so that it was always right to do a work of love on any day. The religious leaders gave the people so many laws to keep that no one could remember them all. Jesus told them that if they remembered to love God with all their hearts and to love their neighbors as themselves, they would be keeping all the laws without having to worry about them.

Jesus knew that most people had more hatred than love in their hearts. Often they did not know why they hated people except that it had always been that way.

For hundreds of years the Samaritans and the Jews had had nothing to do with each other. A traveler from Galilee who wanted to go to Jerusalem could get there most quickly by going through Samaria. But nearly everyone took the longer road on the other side of the Jordan River in order to keep away from Samaria. The Samaritans were surprised when Jesus, a Jew, stayed for some days in Samaria. When he came away, he had some followers there.

Both Samaritans and Jews remembered a story Jesus told one day. A man who thought he knew much more than Jesus asked him what people he should love as his neighbors. Jesus knew that there were some people such as Samaritans that the man did not want to love at all. So he told him a story of a Samaritan who was the only traveler willing to help a man who had been beaten by robbers and left half-dead at the side of the road. A priest and a Levite had hurried by without showing any care for the poor man.

When the story was finished, Jesus looked sharply at the man who had been questioning him and asked him, "Which of the three would you say was neighbor to him who fell among the robbers?"

The man did not like Samaritans, but there was

only one answer he could give. "The one who showed mercy, of course," he said.

"Then go and be that kind of neighbor yourself," said Jesus.

Many who were listening did not like to hear Jesus tell a Jew to be as good a neighbor as a Samaritan had been. But there were others who were glad that Jesus was teaching men to love instead of to hate.

The day came when the disciples were ready to go out by themselves to teach and to heal. It was a happy day for Jesus, for this was the next step in his plan. He had trained the disciples. Now, wherever they went, they would make new disciples for him. Step by step his word would be carried farther and farther until it reached the ends of the earth.

Jesus had decided to send the disciples out in twos, so that each would have another to help him. He had decided also that they should carry his message only to Jews, even though many other people were living in Palestine. For long years God had been making the Jews ready to receive his truth and take it to others. Now was their chance to accept the Gospel and take it to people everywhere.

The disciples were frightened as they thought of all the things that might happen. What if no one would receive them? What if they were unable to heal anyone? What if the Pharisees tripped them up in their teaching as they had tried to do with Jesus?

Jesus warned them that their difficulties would be great. However, they did not need to be afraid. They must trust God for everything and let him lead them every step of the way.

The weeks passed quickly, and the disciples began to return. What stories they had to tell! Many people had received their good news gladly. Many who had been insane with fear were restored to their right minds. Men who were slaves to evil spirits that made their lives a torture were set free. The disciples were very sure now that God was doing all that he had promised long, long ago. He was coming among men in all his power to change their lives and to bring a new day of freedom and joy and peace.

The disciples often wondered about Jesus. He was like a prophet, yet he was greater than any prophet who had ever lived. When he spoke to the people, it was as though God himself were speaking. And then there were the strange and wonderful things he did, the sick people who were made well, the hungry people who were fed. Always he said that it was the power of God that did these things. The disciples did not understand everything Jesus said and did, but one thing they knew—their lives were very different since they had begun to follow him. Long ago Jeremiah had said that the day would come when God would give his people new hearts and make a new covenant with them. It was certain that Jesus was giving men new hearts. Perhaps the day the prophets had hoped for had really come!

When the disciples grew tired, Jesus led them away from the crowded towns of Galilee and up into the quieter mountain country. There they talked of all they had been doing and made plans for the days ahead. And they began to wonder more and more if Jesus could be the Messiah, sent among them to rule for God.

Jesus knew what was in their minds. The time had come for him to share his secret with them.

He asked them, "Who do men say that I am?"

They told him some of the things they had heard. Jesus looked round the circle and into the faces of the men who were waiting for what he would say next. These men had left everything for him. They had shared hunger and hatred and hard work with him.

Gently he asked, "And who do you say that I am?"

Simon answered, his whole face alight with what he was thinking, "You are the Messiah, the Son of the living God."

It was a great joy to Jesus to see the faith of Simon and the others. He told them that God himself had given them such faith. Together with others who believed as they did, they would be a great new people of God for the future. From that day Jesus called Simon by a new name—"Peter," which means "rock."

But he warned them that God's great work could not be done without pain and suffering. People who did not want to change their ways, would try to stop him. If they could not stop him in any other way, they would kill him.

The disciples did not like to hear Jesus say such things. They were sure there was some way to protect him from harm. If he were really the Messiah, then he could not die, for it was written in the Scriptures that the Messiah would be victorious over all his enemies and rule forever.

When Jesus told his followers he had decided to go up to Jerusalem, they tried to persuade him not to go. They were afraid of what might happen there. Already many of the priests and Pharisees were saying that it was not right to let anyone speak as Jesus did. But King Herod and the Romans were dangerous too. They would kill a man in a moment if they thought he might stir up the people to make trouble. None of the disciples could forget that the prophet John had been put to death by Herod—and Jesus spoke even more sharply and boldly than John!

At first it seemed as though some of the Twelve would not go any farther with Jesus. But when they saw that he was not afraid, their faith came back to them and they went with him. They traveled across the Jordan and through the towns in the region beyond, teaching and healing as they went. They did not all stay together, but scattered through many towns and then met again farther on.

Near Jericho they came back across the Jordan and began the journey up through the hills to Jerusalem. With them were followers of Jesus from all parts of the land and other people who had never seen him before but were going up to Jerusalem for the Passover Feast. The disciples could not help wondering what would happen when they reached the city. Jerusalem had been waiting for hundreds of years for God to send the Prince of Peace whose law would go out from their city to rule over all the earth. But now that the

Prince was on his way to the city, they were afraid that the rulers would turn him away.

At last they came to the top of the Mount of Olives. They could look right across the city and see the walls on the other side. There, just inside the wall below them, was the Temple. They could hear the noise of thousands of people in the streets. A steady stream of travelers was moving up the road in the Kidron valley and through the eastern gate.

Now Jesus sent a man to bring a donkey for him to ride. The disciples knew what that meant. It was written in the Scriptures that the Messiah would come to his city riding upon a donkey.

Then began the last stage of the journey, down the hill, up the other side, and into the city. There seemed to be hundreds of people crowded about now, and they were shouting a welcome: "Hosanna, blessed is he who comes in the name of the Lord!" Jesus' secret was no longer hidden. Even the children were calling out that it was the Messiah who had come.

Servants of the high priest who saw and heard what was happening went at once to their master and reported, "A teacher who comes from Galilee is being proclaimed a king by the people."

Soon the high priest heard something more. The teacher from Galilee had gone into the Temple courts and acted as though he were in charge there. He had accused the officers of the high priest of cheating the people and of making the Temple court into a market

place. Not only that, but he had driven out of the Temple the cattle and the sheep which were being sold to the people for sacrifices.

It did not take the high priest and his advisers long to act. They had Jesus watched as he taught in the Temple court day by day. They found one of his disciples, Judas, who was frightened at what Jesus was doing and they persuaded him to betray Jesus into their hands. On the fifth day they had made all their plans. After it was dark, Judas led them out to a garden on the side of the Mount of Olives, where he knew Jesus would be.

Jesus did not seem surprised or frightened when they arrested him. They led him back to the city. The high priest questioned Jesus, but could get no answers from him. He sent him to Pilate, the Roman governor, and Pilate sent him to Herod, accusing him of trying to make himself king. There was no one to speak for Jesus and no one to take his part when they whipped him and mocked him.

The next morning the Roman soldiers led Jesus and two thieves through the streets of the city and out through the gate to a hill overlooking the road. In the crowd that followed were Mary, Jesus' mother, and John, and others of his friends. They could do nothing but watch through their tears as Jesus was crucified with a thief on each side of him. They saw him look down at the soldiers and say, "Father, forgive them, for they know not what they do." He did not speak often, but the words that he spoke they never forgot. And then he died.

The disciples could hardly believe that Jesus was gone from them. They could not understand how it could have happened. Surely the Messiah would not die! Perhaps they had been wrong in believing that he was the Messiah!

Two days passed. Early in the morning of the third day, two women who went to the tomb where the body of Jesus had been laid brought back a strange story. They said that Jesus was not dead but alive, that he had risen from the dead. It was hard for the others to believe. But before the day was over, they all knew that it was true. Jesus was alive, and had been with them and had spoken to them. He was stronger than death. He was stronger than all his enemies. He was indeed the King whom God had promised to send to destroy evil in the hearts of men and to teach the nations of the earth to live under God's rule.

Many times during the days that followed, the disciples saw him. He promised that, though they would not be able to see him, he would be with them always. Some of them would have to suffer even as he had suffered. They would have to travel over land and sea and visit faraway cities. The news must be carried to the ends of the earth and to all people that they need no longer live in darkness. In Jesus and his Gospel the light of the world had come.

13. A New People

IN JERUSALEM everything was just as it had been before. Jews from all over the world were crowding into
the Temple courts every day. They came from Persia
and from Babylonia, from the cities of Asia Minor and
from the far southern cities of Egypt; they came from
Greece and from Rome. For now there were far more
Jews living in other lands than in Palestine. Some of
them belonged to families that had been carried away

193

into exile long years before; others had moved away from Palestine because they found it so hard there to make a living for themselves and their children. Wherever they were, they had synagogues in which they worshiped and listened when the books of the Scriptures were read. But each year many of them journeyed to Jerusalem at the time of the Passover.

These people from other lands did not know what to think of the stories they heard about the teacher from Galilee. He had been in Jerusalem only a few days while they were there, but the whole city was talking about him. The priests were saying that by acting quickly and having him put to death they had saved the city much trouble, for Jesus was a very dangerous revolutionist and he would have turned everything upside down if he had lived. There were others, however, who said that the priests were wrong: Jesus was greater than all the prophets and had spoken for God as no one else ever had.

The priests were very angry when they heard that the disciples were saying Jesus had risen from the dead. They accused the disciples of having stolen the body of Jesus out of the tomb where it was buried and then of telling a lie in saying, "Jesus is not dead, but is alive forevermore." They did not worry too much about it, however. They were sure that soon nearly everyone would forget that Jesus had ever lived.

But Jesus was not forgotten.

There was an upstairs room in one house in Jerusalem where day after day the followers of Jesus gathered to talk of the things he had said and done. It was the room where Jesus had eaten supper with the Twelve the night he was arrested. Sometimes there were only two or three planning together how to carry on Jesus' work. Sometimes there were more than a hundred men and women, and first one, then another, would tell what he remembered of Jesus.

It seemed such a short time since Jesus had begun to preach. It was less than three years since Andrew and John and Simon had met him while they were still followers of the prophet John. There were many who had known him only a few months. They had thought that they would have years and years to work with him and to learn from him. They had dreamed of the great things they could do with him as their leader. But now everything was changed. They had to go on alone. But no! Not alone! For he had promised them that if they trusted in him he would be with them always.

It was hard for the disciples not to be discouraged when they thought how few of them there were and how great a work Jesus had given them to do. They were to go into all parts of the world and teach what they had heard from Jesus, until all men knew the truth as they did. But there were hundreds of cities and countries and millions of people. How could a few disciples hope ever to reach them all?

Then they remembered the time Jesus had been teaching thousands of people who had come out to a place in the country to hear him. They were hungry, and there were only five loaves of bread and a few fishes. When Jesus told the disciples to feed the people, it seemed impossible, but when they went ahead there was enough for all and some to spare. They remembered also that in the time of Abraham and of Moses and of Isaiah and of Jeremiah there were few

196

who really believed, and yet through them God had been able to work out his purpose. It did not seem to matter to God how few he had to begin with, if only they were willing to trust him completely.

Each time the followers of Jesus gathered in the upper room to talk of him, he seemed to them nearer than ever. They began to understand the things he had said and done as they never had understood before.

Often James or Peter or John would say: "How stupid we were not to see what he meant! We were so set in our own ideas that we did not really hear."

John and James remembered the time they had asked Jesus to make them the chief officers of his kingdom when he became king of all the earth. Now they knew that he was a far different kind of king from what they had thought.

Peter remembered how he had told Jesus not to talk of having to suffer, and Jesus had told him to stop making it harder for him to do what he must do. Peter remembered also how, on the night before Jesus died, he had denied that he even knew Jesus so that the soldiers would not arrest him too. Now he was ashamed, for he understood that God sometimes expects those who serve him to endure great suffering.

The more the disciples thought of the way Jesus had endured his suffering, the more they loved him and were willing to risk even their lives in order to carry on what he had begun.

Many of the Jews from other countries were still in Jerusalem seven weeks after the death of Jesus, when the Day of Pentecost was celebrated. Suddenly word went through the streets that something strange was happening in the house where the followers of Jesus met. Quickly a crowd gathered in the street before the house, and some pressed into the courtyard and hallway of the lower floor. They heard what sounded at first to be just a confusion of voices, but as they listened it seemed to each man as though someone were speaking to him in his own language. It was hard to make out the words, but there was something about them that made many of the listeners feel that God was calling them to share in the faith of these followers of Jesus. But there were others who had a different idea.

"These people have been drinking wine and they are out of their minds," they said. "This shows you what kind of people these followers of Jesus are."

Peter went out to the crowd and told them what had happened.

"You do not understand if you think these people are drunken," he said. "The day has come that was promised long ago. God said that he would make his Spirit dwell in the hearts of his people and would do great works through them. It is God who is speaking to you through words of his servants."

Then Peter declared to them how, in Jesus, God had at last sent his people a Saviour. He showed them from the Scriptures that Jesus was the very one of whom the prophets and psalmists had spoken long ago. But when He came, Israel rejected him, and instead of serving him, they had the Romans put him to death.

The people listened quietly to what Peter said because they knew that he was telling them the truth. It seemed to them now that a terrible thing had happened. If what Peter said was true, then what had been done was worse than anything that had ever happened before in all their history. Long ago the kings and many of the people had refused to listen to the prophets. Sometimes they had even killed them. But to kill the Messiah, the Saviour!

Then Peter went on to say: "Let no one make the mistake of thinking that Jesus' enemies have defeated him. God has raised him from the dead and made him Lord over all."

Before Peter had finished, some in the crowd were crying out, "What can we do?"

Peter said, "Repent every one of you and be baptized in the name of Jesus the Messiah, that your sins may be forgiven and that you too may have God's Spirit dwelling in you."

There were many in the crowd who had heard Jesus teach and who knew now that what Peter said was true. But there were many others who had heard little or nothing of Jesus before. That day three thousand of them decided that they must become followers of Jesus, even though the priests and the Pharisees and many of their friends would have nothing more to do with them.

No longer could Jesus' followers meet in the upstairs room, for there were now too many for that. They gathered in different homes to study and pray and talk together. The disciples whom Jesus had trained were busy every day teaching the new followers or preaching the Gospel in the Temple courts or in the synagogues as Jesus had done.

Some of the followers were very poor. Some had to leave their families and their work because the others in their homes, and the people for whom they worked, thought Jesus' teaching was wrong. But none of them were ever without food or a place to sleep. One of the things Jesus had always said was that if his disciples had God's love in their hearts, they would share whatever they had with those who were in need.

When the priests and the chief men of the city saw that Jesus' followers were increasing instead of becoming fewer in number, they hardly knew what to do. If they did nothing, the disciples would win more and more people; but if they punished them, it seemed only to make them bolder. They locked Peter and John in prison, and the next day, when they brought them before the council, Peter began preaching the Gospel to the members of the council and trying to persuade even them to become disciples of Jesus.

One of the leaders in the council, a teacher named Gamaliel, did not agree with those who thought that Peter and John should be put to death.

"Be careful what you do," he said to the others. "If these men are merely troublemakers, they will soon come to a bad end like many others of that kind. But if they are doing God's work, you will be able to do nothing against them because you will be fighting against God."

The members of the council listened to Gamaliel and decided to take his advice. But before they let Peter and John go, they had them beaten with lashes and ordered them to speak no more in the name of Jesus.

Peter's answer to them was, "We must obey God rather than men."

One of the boldest of those who were preaching in Jerusalem was Stephen. He had great power to persuade men, and often when he spoke in the synagogues, the leaders argued with him but were not able to get the better of him. When he said that Jesus' word was greater than the word of Moses, they accused him of not believing in the Scriptures. When he told them that if Jerusalem rejected God's word the city would soon be destroyed, they called him a traitor and accused him of speaking against his own city. They thought Stephen was almost as dangerous as Jesus had been, so they arrested him and brought him before the council.

Stephen, when they questioned him, accused them of rebelling against God and rejecting the Messiah whom He had sent to them. Beginning with the time of Abraham and Moses, he showed them that Israel had always been slow to believe and had refused to hear the servants God sent to speak to them. They had done to Jesus exactly what their fathers before them did to the prophets.

The council no longer had any patience with Stephen, but ordered him to be taken out and stoned to death. Stephen went with them quietly, and they were surprised that he seemed almost happy. He seemed to think that he was going at once to be with his Master, Jesus. Just before he died, he knelt down and prayed for those who were putting him to death, saying, "Lord, lay not this sin to their charge."

A member of the Jewish council named Saul stood near by watching what happened. He saw the look of joy on Stephen's face and heard his words, but he could not understand what they meant. Saul was sure that the high priest and the chief men of the city were right. Unless these followers of Jesus could be stopped, the faith of their fathers would perish from the earth, and the nation would be destroyed. Saul loved Jerusalem and he loved the religion of his people. He had learned it first in his home in Tarsus, far in the north, and then from his teachers in Jerusalem. He would give anything—he would even die—for his religion. It made him angry that this Jesus had upset the faith of so many of the people. The followers of such a man must be crushed.

And yet there was a voice far, far back in Saul's mind that said: "What if Stephen is right? What if Jesus really is the Messiah? What if you are fighting against God's own servant?" Then Saul remembered the story that Jesus had risen from the dead. That was certainly a lie, he thought. And if that was a lie, then all these men were liars and cheats. Yes! The chief priest was right. They must be stopped.

From that time Saul was appointed to arrest all who spoke in the name of Jesus. He became more feared than any other man in Jerusalem. The followers of Jesus tried to escape him by moving away to other places. Some went south into Egypt. Some took ship to Cyprus and Antioch. Others went north by land and found safety for a time in Damascus. Wherever they went they could not be quiet, but told others of the wonderful new life they had found through faith in Jesus. Soon word came back to Jerusalem of what was happening. Everywhere they went these people were persuading others to become followers of Jesus.

Saul went to the high priest and secured permission to go to Damascus and bring back the followers of Jesus who had fled there. He took other men with him to help, because he expected to have many prisoners.

They went down through the hills to Jericho, across the Jordan, and then northward on the Damascus road. They talked as they rode along, but as the days passed Saul had less and less to say. He could not tell the others what was on his mind. He was wondering—somehow he could not keep from wondering: "Am I doing right? Could it be that I am wrong and that these people are right?" It puzzled him that, even when he put them in prison and had them beaten, they spoke kindly to him and seemed sure that God was with them. But each time these thoughts came up in his mind, Saul pushed them back and told himself that what he was doing must be right.

"It makes me think of Abraham going out from his
old home and not knowing where God was leading
him," said the man who had spoken before. "But we
are nearer than Abraham was to seeing the promise
come true."

They made plans together for what they would do
when the ship reached Antioch. Then as evening drew
near they called the children to sit with them and they
sang a hymn. When the hymn was finished, their
leader spoke again.

"Some of you are anxious and troubled about how we are going to live when we reach Antioch," he said. "I remember a saying of Jesus that I often heard from the apostles: 'Do not be anxious what you shall eat or drink. Your life is more than food and your body is more than clothing. Behold the birds of the heaven: they sow not, neither do they reap, nor gather into barns; and your heavenly Father feeds them. Are you not worth much more than they? Seek first God's Kingdom and his righteousness and all that you need will be provided for you.' "

Then, when they had prayed together, they took food out of their bundles and had supper.

The next few days were busy ones for all. When they were safely ashore, they first had to find homes. The men and boys were quick to get work to do. They did not go to the synagogue for worship on the Sabbath, as they had always done in Jerusalem, for they were afraid that they might have trouble again. Rather, they gathered in one of the homes and worshiped by themselves.

Soon their neighbors, who were not Jews at all but gentiles, became friendly with them. Never before had they met people as thoughtful and as unselfish as these believers in Jesus. When the gentiles were invited to join with the believers in worship, some of them came; and when they heard what Jesus had said and done, they became believers too. These gentiles then brought their friends with them, so that the

Church in Antioch grew quickly. The gentiles spoke Greek, and their name for the Messiah was "the Christ." As the people of Antioch heard Jesus' followers talking continually of the Christ, they began to call them "Christians."

When word reached the apostles in Jerusalem of what was happening in Antioch, they were glad. But they were also afraid that the gentiles, who had never known the books of the Law and the Prophets, might not understand the Christian way rightly. The apostles therefore sent one of their leaders named Barnabas to Antioch to teach the new Christians the Gospel as the apostles understood it.

So many people in Antioch wanted to become Christians that Barnabas had more than he could do. He could not find enough teachers. Then one day he remembered that Saul, who was also called Paul, was at his old home in Tarsus, not more than a hundred miles from Antioch by sea. Barnabas went at once to Tarsus, and soon he had Paul as his best assistant in the Church at Antioch.

The new Church sometimes had visitors from Jerusalem. There was great excitement when a letter came saying that Peter was on his way and would soon arrive. The Jews who had come from Jerusalem were glad that they would see Peter again and hear him preach. The gentiles were eager to meet him because he had a part in so much that they had heard about and in so many of the stories about Jesus. They knew that he had been one of the first of the disciples of Jesus—had been the first of them to confess Jesus as the Messiah—and that he had almost lost his faith when Jesus died. They knew the whole story of Peter, and now they would see the man himself.

When Peter came, no one was disappointed. He told the gentiles that long ago God had shown him in a vision that the Gospel was for Jews and gentiles alike. He had baptized the Roman centurion Cornelius, and all his family. He had preached to gentiles in many places in Palestine.

Then an unhappy thing happened. Some men came from Jerusalem who did not think that Jewish Christians and gentile Christians should eat together. They said that the gentiles should be made to keep all the old Jewish laws about eating and drinking before they should be allowed to sit at the same table with Jews. Paul did not agree with them. He told them the only thing that mattered was for men to believe in Jesus Christ and obey him with their whole heart. Peter, however, did not know what to do. He did not want to offend the men from Jerusalem and others who thought as they did. So at last he decided he would eat only with Jews.

When Paul saw what Peter was doing, he went to
him at once.

"Peter," he said to him, "how can you go back on
what you told us? What will the gentiles think? First
you said that the Gospel is for all alike, and now you
refuse to sit at a table with gentiles."

That day it was Paul, and not Peter, to whom most
of the people listened. And after a time even Peter
saw that he had been wrong and that Paul had been
right.

Another visitor from Jerusalem was Agabus, but he brought bad news. When they asked him to speak to the Church, he told of a time of famine that was coming in Judea which would make it hard for the Christians there to live. At once it was decided that all the Christians in Antioch would set aside money each week to be sent to their fellow Christians in Judea. Already they had learned to care for those among themselves who were poor or sick or in any need. Now they realized that they must care for Christians who were far away and whom they had never seen. When the money was ready, Paul and Barnabas took it to Jerusalem. There they reported to the apostles all that was being done in Antioch.

Christians had gone to many other parts of the world besides Antioch. There were little Churches in Egypt and even beyond Egypt, along the northern shore of Africa. From Damascus, Christians had gone eastward to Mesopotamia and to Persia. Some had sailed westward to Rome, the great city from which the Romans ruled almost the whole world. Wherever they went, the Christians were only a few people among thousands, but each year they grew in number and more people heard their story.

In Antioch, as the years passed, Paul and Barnabas began to think of new work to do. They told the Christians that it was not enough that the Church was growing every year in Antioch. To the west of Anti-

215

och in Asia Minor were great cities where no one had ever heard of Jesus. Someone must go from Antioch and carry the news of the Gospel westward.

The Christians in the Church at Antioch loved Paul and Barnabas, who had led them so well, but when they had prayed about the matter, they were sure that God wanted them to send their two best leaders for the new work. Paul and Barnabas at once made ready and set out on the journey.

That was the beginning of many journeys for Paul. He climbed the mountain roads to cities where no Christian had ever gone before. Sometimes he slept by the roadside. Sometimes he had no food to eat for days. If there was a synagogue in the city, he went there first and told his fellow Jews the story of the Gospel. Many were glad to hear it, but others were angry when they heard Paul's story and drove him out of their city. More than once he was beaten and nearly lost his life. Often he was put in prison. But he kept going on from city to city, and almost always when he left a place there were a few believers meeting together in one of the homes. Whenever he stayed more than a few days in a city, he found work at his trade, as a maker of tents, in order to pay his way.

On his journeys Paul kept moving westward, and crossed from Asia Minor into Europe. He stayed many months in the cities of Greece, and founded Churches in many of them. He wanted to go on westward to Rome, but he was not able to do so, at that time.

Paul did one important thing to encourage Christians in places that he had visited. He wrote letters to them. When they had problems and difficulties, they would send a letter or a messenger to him to ask what they should do. When his answer arrived, they would read it to the whole congregation, and it was almost as though Paul himself were there speaking to them.

In Corinth, after Paul left, the Christians became divided between different leaders. They had heard not only Paul, but also Peter and Apollos. Some said, "We belong with Peter." Others said, "We belong with Apollos," or, "We belong with Paul." They would no longer work together at all. Paul wrote to them and told them to forget him and Apollos and Peter and to think only of Christ; then they would be able to love and understand each other. They were very much ashamed when they heard Paul's words, especially when they came to a part of the letter which said that if they did not have God's love in their hearts, they were of no use at all to God. They knew that each of them had been so interested in proving himself right and the others wrong that they had ceased to love one another.

When the people of another Church near by heard that a letter had come from Paul to Corinth or to Philippi, they had a copy of it made which they could read in their Church too. In this way copies of Paul's letters began to be read in many Churches in many places.

Because Paul was not able to get to Rome, he wrote a long letter to the Christians at Rome, telling them how he understood the Gospel. What he said in the letter was what he would have preached to them if he had been with them.

In it he told them all that he knew and understood about the good news of Christ, and the way in which he wanted that good news told everywhere. In the letter he wrote just what he would have told them if he had been able to visit them. They could not forget his words.

After many years Paul traveled to Rome, but not in the way he expected. While he was in Jerusalem on a visit, he was arrested, and was sent to Rome as a prisoner. He was shipwrecked on the way and had many adventures, but, best of all, he won some of those who were traveling with him to believe in Jesus as he did. In Rome, though he was a prisoner, he lived in a private house and was able to see his friends. Even people from the emperor's palace came to hear his Gospel. When he had time, he wrote more letters to his Churches in Greece and Asia.

Because the Christians refused to worship the Roman gods, the Roman emperor and his officers did not like them. The emperor was afraid that if they disobeyed him in this, they would disobey him in other things and make trouble for him. The Christians said that Christ was their only Lord, and that they must obey his word in all things.

All over the empire Christians now found the Roman officials more and more unfriendly to them. They were arrested in great numbers and put to death. One of those who died in Rome was Paul.

Until this time, whenever Christians met there was usually someone present who had seen and heard Jesus, or had heard one of the apostles tell the story of what Jesus had said and done. Many of Jesus' sayings had also been written down so that they could be used in teaching new Christians. But now, as few of the older Christians remained alive, it was important to write down the story just as the apostles had told it, so that it would never be forgotten. The first person to do this was Mark, who remembered what he had heard from Peter and others and wrote it all as briefly as possible. Copies of his book were made until nearly every Church had one.

There were many stories of Jesus that Mark left out of his book. So at a later time Luke gathered these together and, using Mark's book as well, wrote the whole story over again in the best way he could. Elsewhere another writer was at work doing the same thing, and when it was finished, it was The Gospel According to Matthew.

Still later, a fourth writer told the story in a way different from any of the others. What he wanted to show more than anything else was how God's love came down to earth in Jesus, and how it opened the way to a new world of peace and joy for all who would receive him. Because the writer's name was John, the book was called The Gospel According to John.

It had been a long time since Jesus had lived and died, but he was not being forgotten. There were more people now who knew him and loved him than had seen him during his lifetime. When his followers talked of him, he did not seem far away. And when they did as he commanded them to do, feeding the hungry, caring for the sick and unhappy, telling the good news of God's forgiveness to those who had done evil, they felt that Jesus himself was right with them. But it was when they had to suffer for their faith that he seemed nearest of all.

Ever since Jesus had risen from the dead, his followers had been sure that soon he would come back to them to defeat everything that was evil and to establish peace and truth and justice over the whole earth. As the years passed and he did not return, they did not give up their hope. They knew that God's love was stronger than all the selfishness and hatred and greed of men. One by one men were being gathered into the Church of Jesus Christ.

221

It might take hundreds of years; it might take thousands of years; but the day would come when men everywhere would know that Christ was their only true King. Then there would be one great family of God: God had promised it to Abraham; he had promised it to Moses; he had promised it to all the prophets. Often it has seemed as though it would never come true. But, since Christ came, all who believed in him knew that God was keeping his promise.

SCRIPTURE REFERENCES

The Bible contains many books. Because *A Promise to Keep* can tell only the most important parts of the story that is found in these books, you will often want to read more of the story as it is written in the Bible itself. This list will help you.

There are the old, old stories of the beginnings:

The Creation: Genesis, chs. 1;2. Compare this with Job, ch. 38, and Psalm 104.

The Sins of Man: Genesis, chs. 3; 4:1–13; 6 to 8; 11:1–9, tell of self-will, envy, evil living, pride.

The patriarchs were men chosen by God to do great things. They were:

Abraham: Genesis 12:1–7; chs. 13; 21:1–5; 22:1–18.

Isaac: Genesis, chs. 24; 26:17–33.

Jacob: Genesis 27:1–45; 28:10–22; chs. 32; 33.

Joseph: Genesis, chs. 37; 41:1 to 46:7.

Moses: Exodus 1:6–14; 3:1–12; chs. 5:1 to 6:8; 7:1 to 20:21; 24:1 to 25:9; 35; 40; Numbers 3:1–10; chs. 13:1 to 14:24; 26:1, 2, 63–65; Deuteronomy, chs. 31; 34.

Joshua: Joshua, chs. 1 to 4; 22 to 24.

When, under Joshua's leadership, the Children of Israel had again conquered the Land of Canaan, they were advised in peace and in war by wise men and women known as "judges." Here are stories about several of them:

Deborah: Judges, ch. 4.

Gideon: Judges, chs. 6 to 8.

Samuel: I Samuel, chs. 1 to 3; 8.

After the people demanded and were given a king, they had a long succession of good and bad rulers. The Bible does not tell all about each one, but it does tell what kind of king each one was in words like these: II Kings 15:3; II Kings 14:24.

Here are some stories of a very few of the kings:

Saul: I Samuel, chs. 9 to 12; 15; 31.

David: I Samuel, chs. 16 to 20; 25; II Samuel 5:1–12; 6:1–15; chs. 7; 9; 11; 12; 21 to 24; I Kings 2:1–10.

Solomon: I Kings 2:12; chs. 3; 4: 21–34; 5; 6; 8:1–21.

Rehoboam and Jeroboam: I Kings, chs. 12; 15:1–6, 25–30.

Ahab: I Kings 16:29–33; chs. 21; 22:34–40.

Hezekiah: II Kings, chs. 18 to 20.

Josiah: II Kings, chs. 22:1 to 23:28.

223

When the kings forgot God's will, men called prophets reminded them of it, even at the risk of their lives. Here are some instances of this:

Elijah: I Kings, chs. 17 to 19;
II Kings, chs. 1; 2.
Elisha: II Kings, chs. 2:1 to 13:20.
Micaiah: I Kings, ch. 22.

Listen to some of these men of God as they speak:

Nehemiah 1:1 to 7:3; ch. 8.
Isaiah 40:27-31.
Jeremiah 10:23, 24.
Ezekiel 34:11-16.
Hosea 14:9.
Joel 2:21-25.
Amos 5:14, 15.
Obadiah 15.
Micah 6:8.
Nahum 1:3, 5-7.
Habakkuk 3:19.
Zephaniah 3:9.
Haggai 2:6-9.
Zechariah 7:8-14.
Malachi 2:10; 3:1-3.

After Jerusalem had been destroyed and its people taken as captives to Babylon, they were at last allowed to go back to rebuild their homes and Temple under capable leaders.

Other men, led of God, added to the story. They were singers, wise men, storytellers.

Songs, read Psalms 1; 8; 19; 23; 24; 67; 100; 103; 119:97-104; 121; 148. Also Song of Solomon 2:11, 12.

Sayings of the Wise, read Proverbs 10:12; 11:28; 12:22; 15:1; 17:22; 19:17; 22:1; 26:27; 31:10, 28. Also Ecclesiastes 12:13, 14.

Stories, read the books of Esther; Ruth; Jonah; Job, chs. 1; 2; 42; Daniel, chs. 1; 3; 6.

Sometimes the prophets spoke of a coming Messiah, God's own King. For his story, turn to the four *Gospels*.

After the crucifixion and resurrection of Jesus, his friends began to carry out his last command (see Matthew 28:19, 20, and Mark 16:15). You can read much of their story in *The Acts of the Apostles*.

As the story of Jesus was spread abroad, first by his friends and followers, then by Paul, and later by other believers, letters of instruction and encouragement went from church to church. Some parts of these letters, especially interesting for you, are:

Romans 10:12-15.
I Corinthians 13:4-8a.*
Galatians 5:14, 22, 23.
Ephesians 6:1-4, 13-17.
Philippians 4:8.
Colossians 3:12-17.
I Thessalonians 4:13-18.
I Timothy 4:12.
II Timothy 2:15.
Titus 3:8.
Hebrews 13:2.
James 3:7, 8, 17, 18.
I Peter 3:10-12.
I John 4:7, 8.

In a time of great suffering, one of the friends of Jesus wrote to Christians who faced torture and death that he might encourage them. He told them of a vision he had had of God's Kingdom. You can read a part of it in Revelation, ch. 21.

From the Moffatt translation.

3302